The
BIRDS
of Sutherland

Alan Vittery

Illustrations by Dave Pullan

Colin Baxter Photography, Grantown-on-Spey, Scotland

To Bonnie

First published in Great Britain in 1997 by

Colin Baxter Photography Ltd
Grantown-on-Spey,
Scotland PH26 3NA

Text © Alan Vittery 1997
Illustrations © Dave Pullan 1997
Maps © Alan Vittery 1997

Synoptic charts on pages 17, 33, 98, 119 © Crown Copyright
Reproduced by permission of the Controller of HMSO.

A CIP catalogue for this book is available from the British Library

ISBN 1-900455-18-8

Front Cover Photograph: Laurie Campbell
Back Cover Photograph: Colin Baxter

Printed in the UK by The Cromwell Press, Wiltshire.

The
BIRDS
of Sutherland

To Alan & Pam

with best wishes

Alan

May, 1997

Contents

Foreword

Sutherland has long been a magic region for those fired with enthusiasm for northern birds. From the days of Charles St. John's Tour in 1848, it became an area to which collectors journeyed from afar, to enrich their cabinets of bird skins and eggs with choice specimens plundered from moor, loch and seacliff. The county formed a major part of the first of the inspired series of regional *Faunas of Scotland*, launched by John Harvie-Brown. This volume, written jointly with Thomas Buckley in 1887, contained enticing descriptions of Sutherland's wild places, and a splendid atmospheric engraving of the mighty walls of Handa with their myriad seafowl, towering from the Atlantic. Victorian depredations saw the last of the Sea Eagle and Osprey, but Sutherland remained celebrated for its Golden Eagles, Black and Red-throated Divers, and Greenshanks. The early bird photographers were drawn here by such glamorous subjects.

My first view of Sutherland was in April 1952, when I cycled from Lairg station to Kylesku in the west. Ten days of roaming the rugged uplands left the impression of a gloriously wild and untrodden land where Nature reigned supreme. In later years I explored some of the desolate and sombre moorlands of the east, where Sutherland marches with Caithness, and a bird fauna of arctic tundra affinities has found an extensive breeding ground.

Knowledge of Sutherland's birds grew steadily from the 1960s. There were counts of some more notable species – Peregrine, Golden Eagle and the colonial nesting seabirds. Colonisation by new northern breeders was reported – Wood Sandpiper, Brambling, Redwing and Fieldfare, while Dotterel and Snow Bunting were again seen more regularly on the higher hills and Ospreys returned to nest, so far only in trees. Desmond Nethersole-Thompson and his family began their long-term study of Greenshanks in a wild mountain glen.

Modern 'progress' began to alter the Sutherland scene after 1945, bringing conservation problems in its wake. First were the works of hydro-engineers in transforming the catchments of the Oykel and Shin. Then the episode of organochlorine seed dressings and sheep dips showed that even birds in wilderness country could be under threat. There were earlier tree plantations, but from 1980 the foresters began to smother the lower peaty moorlands with their conifer thickets, and one of wildlife conservation's more desperate battles ensued.

For long the interest was mainly in breeders, but diligent observation has more recently extended records of passage migrants and casual visitors, and revealed the importance of Sutherland for its other birds. Pioneer sea-watcher Alan Vittery came to live in the county in 1990 and has led this expansion of knowledge. He is thus extremely well placed to present this most appropriate and nicely balanced up-dating of Sutherland ornithology with the present volume. It is an important addition to the literature, and will be an invaluable guide to those who – more numerously nowadays – are drawn to the north in search of birds.

Dr Derek Ratcliffe
January, 1997

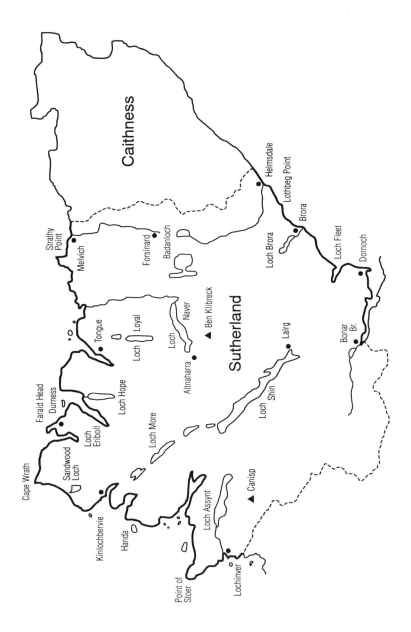

Introduction

There are few parts of the British Isles as wild, remote and little known as much of Sutherland, which occupies the northern extremity of the mainland with the exception of the north-eastern tip (Caithness). Rocky coasts in the west and north contrast with the soft, sandier shoreline of the Moray Firth. Geologically complex and ancient mountain ranges rise to over 1000m in the west. Undulating peat bogs cover great tracts of the hinterland, whilst drier heather moorland predominates in the east. Add to these uncountable lochs, rivers and burns, plus relict woodlands, and you have a county rich in diversity.

With sea on three sides and proximity to the Gulf Stream, Sutherland enjoys a milder climate than might be supposed from its latitude. Atlantic depressions bring frequent rain and high winds, particularly to the west. The springs tend to be cool and the summers damp, although late May and June are sometimes favoured by a high pressure system centred over the eastern Atlantic. Except in the coldest winters, snow rarely lies at lower levels for more than a few days at a time.

The county's importance as the stronghold of some of Britain's rarest breeding species, such as Black-throated Diver and Greenshank, is well known. The attempt in the late 1980s to protect from afforestation the tundra-like 'Flow Country', with its high breeding densities of wading birds and small populations of such species as Common Scoter and Wood Sandpiper, was a conservation cause célèbre. Sutherland also boasts huge seabird colonies on the rocky coasts and islands of the north-west and has thriving populations of birds of prey, including Buzzard, Peregrine, Merlin, Golden Eagle and, increasingly, Osprey. In addition, the Moray Firth holds internationally important numbers of seabirds, waders and wildfowl, many of which feed on the Sutherland coast.

The only modern work on its avifauna, *Sutherland Birds*, was published 14 years ago (Angus 1983). Whilst much of the county appears unaltered since then, our knowledge of its birds, particularly in respect of migration patterns, has greatly increased. Changes in the populations and distribution of some species have undoubtedly occurred. These have been caused by habitat change (such as blanket afforestation) and by more natural,

9

longer-term factors such as climatic amelioration. There have been both losses and gains. This book takes stock of these changes and analyses the data accumulated since 1982 to provide a detailed, up-to-date account of the status of Sutherland's birds.

Although much of Sutherland accords with the tourist's vision of 'wilderness', few parts of the county are natural in the sense that the habitat has been unaffected by man's activities. After the end of the last Ice Age the great Caledonian Forest extended into much of the southern half of the county. Only tiny remnants now survive, most notably at Amat in the extreme south. Recent re-afforestation with alien conifers has failed to provide a substitute for the specialised species, such as Crested Tit and Capercaillie, dependent on the ancient forest. Unfortunately the new plantations are mainly concentrated in the central peatlands, which have been naturally treeless for thousands of years and support a number of nationally rare breeding birds. These are, without exception, threatened by tree planting. This reduces the area of open bog, lowers the water table over a wide area, increases the acidity of water bodies and provides secure refuges for Hooded Crows and mammalian predators, which take their toll of both eggs and young and can seriously reduce breeding success.

In areas where climax birch woodland naturally occurs, overgrazing by deer, sheep and rabbits prevents regeneration. These woodlands are moribund and will not survive far into the next century. Only protection and re-planting, now possible under the Forestry Authority's Woodland Grants Scheme, or a drastic change in the land management regime, will save them.

Bird Habitats

Apart from the birch woodlands and the Caledonian pinewood remnants already mentioned, oakwoods occur on some south facing slopes in the south, as at Spinningdale. The extensive alder carr at The Mound, accidentally created in the nineteenth century when a new route to the north round Loch Fleet was constructed, is now a National Nature Reserve. Widely scattered rowans provide an autumn berry bonanza for thrushes. Plantations of Scots pine offer some scope for native birds such as the Scottish Crossbill, but most recent planting is of sitka spruce and lodgepole pine. Some of the young plantations attract Whinchats, Black Grouse, Short-eared Owls and Hen Harriers but, once the canopy has closed, they are of little value to birds, except for already common species such as Coal Tit and Goldcrest.

The relatively dry, heather-clad hills of the south-east are managed for grouse. They support a breeding population of Golden Plovers but relatively few other waders. Blue Hares attract hunting Golden Eagles in winter and the huge numbers of Meadow Pipits provide food for Merlins and Hen Harriers. Late muirburn is the principal threat in these areas, apart from the continuing (illegal) persecution of some birds of prey.

Further west the proportion of heather to moor grass and deer sedge decreases. Peaty dubh lochans, in themselves rather sterile, provide breeding sites for Red-throated Divers and a few wildfowl. The density of breeding waders, such as Dunlin, increases in the undulating 'flows' to the north – a tundra-like habitat attracting species of sub-Arctic origins. Whilst Greenshanks also nest here, their preference is for drier, morainic ground, though they feed by rivers, pools and lochs of all sizes, as well as on coasts if accessible.

In the extreme west, the inhospitable terrain and exceptionally high rainfall combine to pose problems for many would-be breeders. The characteristically 'knobbly' outcrops of Lewisian gneiss and their associated lochs and lochans hold good populations of Black-throated Diver and Greenshank. The harshness of the topography is partly offset by the relative mildness of the climate. Quite extensive deciduous woodlands, mainly of birch and rowan, survive in places. The only recent study of their birds

11

was carried out in 1970/71 (Yapp 1974). A new survey is needed, particularly in view of the fairly rapid spread of new colonists from the south and east.

Fell-fields and stony mountain tops in central and western Sutherland provide refuges for Ptarmigan, Snow Bunting and Dotterel. This fragile habitat and its associated flora and fauna are most at risk from global warming.

The rocky west and north coasts are best known for their seabird colonies. Handa Island, with its auks and skuas, was formerly an RSPB Reserve. It is now managed by the Scottish Wildlife Trust. The Torridonian sandstone cliffs of Clo Mor (the highest on the Scottish mainland) have one of the largest Puffin colonies in Britain. A few uninhabited islands host breeding colonies of Storm Petrels and provide winter grazing for flocks of Barnacle Geese.

The wetlands of Sutherland fall into many categories, from estuaries, sea lochs and huge freshwater bodies like Loch Shin to the 'patterned bogs' of the Flow Country. Freshwater reedmarsh is a scarce commodity – a few lochs are reed-fringed, the Kyle of Sutherland contains one remnant near Invershin and, in the west, there are small areas at Scourie and Clachtoll (Stoer). The river flood plain between Invershin and Rosehall holds good numbers of wildfowl in mild winters. Outside the breeding season, marine habitats are richer in bird life in the east, where the estuaries are less scoured by storms. Inland waters, with the exception of the Kyle of Sutherland, do not normally hold large numbers of waterfowl apart from roosting Greylags.

Although most of the 'special' breeders are found in the remoter areas of the hinterland, the north and the west, the visiting birder touring Sutherland will be struck by the relative abundance of birds in the southeast, with its more varied habitat and softer landscapes. The richer agricultural areas on the coast and in the larger straths, as well as the main settlements, attract large numbers of the commoner species, which are often scarce, or even absent, in the west.

Land-Use Changes

Much of Sutherland continues to be managed as it has been for most of the last two centuries: for sheep and game (principally deer, grouse, salmon and trout). Agriculture has not been intensified to any great extent, although further 'improvement' of marginal land through drainage and re-seeding continues steadily. This may be a factor in the decline of some of the breeding waders like Redshank and Snipe, although this is much less marked than further south in Britain.

One single land use has had a dramatic effect on the wildlife of the hinterland in the last thirty years – forestry. Large areas of blanket bog, a habitat scarce in world terms for which Britain has a major international responsibility, have been needlessly sacrificed in the cause of tax avoidance, benefiting only a few individuals. Changes in the fiscal regime in the late 1980s came too late to save many areas rich in peatland specialities and prevent the blight of such pristine tracts as Glen Oykel and the Strathy River. That first breathtaking view of Suilven from the eastern approach will be seriously tarnished for future generations. Recent relaxation of the controls on new planting outside designated Sites of Special Scientific Interest (SSSI) inevitably means more open ground will be lost in the years to come, hopefully on a much smaller scale.

The new plantations are not without ornithological benefits in their early years but the species which exploit them are not of such significance as those driven out. Golden Eagle, Golden Plover, Dunlin, Greenshank, Red Grouse, Ring Ouzel and Raven are among those adversely affected. The first small plantations appeared in Sutherland as long ago as the late eighteenth century. By 1845 over 2023 ha (5000 acres) had been planted, almost all in the south-east. In 1961 the total was still below 10,117 ha (25,000 acres), compared to just over 50,000 ha (c. 125,000 acres) today.

On the credit side, the much-needed regeneration of native woodland is at last under way. There has been an encouragingly rapid take-up of the Forestry Authority's Woodland Grants Scheme and, on a smaller scale, Scottish Natural Heritage has entered into agreements, so far covering 142 ha (351 acres), with some Estates owning SSSIs.

The decline in traditional crofting in the second half of the twentieth century has reduced habitat diversity in both coastal areas and the straths. Indeed, Sutherland must have been a much more hospitable region to those species closely associated with agriculture and other forms of human activity (such as waste disposal) before the Clearances! Crofters, encouraged by generous subsidies (which result in over-stocking of the land), have increasingly become sheep farmers. Consequently, the cereal patch and swede and potato crops, attractive to both granivorous and invertebrate-eating birds, have become a rare sight. This no doubt helped to accelerate the local decline of the Corncrake and reduced winter feeding opportunities for species like the Twite.

The only other 'land use' to have had a significant effect on the county during this period, apart from tourism with its associated infrastructure, has been nature conservation. No new National Nature Reserves have been created to add to the seven already in existence in the 1960s but the number of SSSI has increased to a total of 78, 30 of which are on the peatlands. These cover in total over 173,000 ha (427,480 acres). Whilst it provides only limited protection, SSSI status at least guarantees early warning of any proposed change in land use.

Handa Island became an RSPB nature reserve in 1962 under an agreement with the owners, Mr J.C. and Dr Jean Balfour. (It is now managed by the Scottish Wildlife Trust.) In 1970 the Loch Fleet Reserve was established by the Scottish Wildlife Trust. In 1994 the Woodland Trust acquired 1756 acres (710 ha) at Ledmore and Migdale Woods, to the north of the Dornoch Firth, and in 1995 the RSPB purchased the 17,600 acre (7123 ha) Forsinard Estate. This last will help to protect some of the rarer breeders and has already proved a major attraction to British and foreign tourists, and to schoolchildren.

Fish farms proliferated in the 1970s and 80s and may have consequences for wildlife in freshwater lochs through changes in water chemistry and their possible effect on invertebrates and wild fish populations. Their impact on the birds of sea lochs will vary according to the nature of the water flow. In both inland and sea lochs, species taking advantage of the unnatural abundance of food may suffer increased persecution.

Breeding Specialities

The Highlands of Scotland is the most important region in Britain for scarce breeding birds, providing a climatic niche for species of mainly sub-Arctic range to maintain viable populations. The higher the latitude, the lower the altitude at which montane species occur. So, although Sutherland cannot boast mountain blocks quite as high as the Cairngorms, it does host many of the specialities associated with that area. A visitor from the south may be most struck by the variety and abundance of birds of prey. The largely depopulated interior provides the huge, open ranges required by Golden Eagles. Buzzards breed at quite high densities in the lower areas and Hen Harriers are less persecuted than in the heavily keepered grouse moors of the Grampians. Ospreys again seem secure after their extinction in the nineteenth century. I have seen no fewer than 16 species of diurnal raptor from my house near Brora in the last six years, half of which are resident in the area!

If I had to choose a bird to represent the county, it would have to be either Black-throated Diver or Greenshank. Sutherland holds over fifty pairs of the former and is the undisputed national headquarters of the latter with something in excess of 350 pairs. Red-throated Divers outnumber their larger congeners and other species of wader are present in nationally important numbers, particularly in the lochan rich 'Flow Country'. Several rarer waders, such as Whimbrel, Wood Sandpiper and Dotterel, maintain a toehold and there is always the possibility of chancing on Purple Sandpiper, Temminck's Stint, Green Sandpiper, Turnstone, or...who knows?

The vast seabird colonies are of global importance. Breeding wildfowl include some of the last indigenous Greylags, Wigeon, Common Scoters and Goldeneye (a very recent colonist). It seems only a matter of time before Scaup is found nesting again. A few Corncrakes are still reported in most years in the north-west and singing Spotted Crakes should be listened for on summer nights.

Climatic amelioration is thought to be mainly responsible for the north-westerly spread of a number of species in the last century, despite a cooling of Arctic regions since about 1950 (perhaps offset at our latitude by global warming). Some of these, such as Garden Warbler, Blackcap and Scarlet Rosefinch, are still in the process of colonising. Others are likely to follow early in the new Millennium if global warming follows current predictions.

In apparent contradiction of this trend, more colonists, actual and potential, come from the north-east: Redwing, Fieldfare, Brambling and Red-backed Shrike (presumably from the Scandinavian population) have already bred. Bluethroat and Icterine Warbler may soon do so. Thrush Nightingale (which has recently reached southern Norway) is another contender. The greater incidence of easterly winds in May (displacing Scandinavia-bound migrants) will help westward-spreading species to overcome the barrier of the North Sea more quickly than they might otherwise have done so.

Even America might provide a new breeder. Spotted Sandpiper has already bred in western Scotland and Pectoral Sandpiper has displayed over the 'flows'. How long will it be before a pair of Ring-billed Gulls are found in a Common Gull colony?

Migration

It seems strange that many of the rarer migrants from the Continent (and beyond) which regularly occur in the Northern Isles in spring and/or autumn are very scarce or absent in Sutherland. This is no doubt partly due to lack of observer coverage, particularly on the north coast, and the absence of an obvious focus for new arrivals, such as an eastern promontory or a strategic offshore island. The main factor, however, is that eastern Sutherland lies in the 'shadow' of the north-east shoulder of Scotland. 'Drift' migrants, blown off course from the east and south east, are intercepted before they reach Sutherland. Most of those arriving north of the shadow find themselves in Caithness or the Northern Isles. As a result, the total number of species on the Sutherland list is lower than might be expected. Occasionally, as in late May 1996, the weather systems combine to produce a sizeable 'fall'. Such occurrences have become more regular in recent years with the establishment of a spring anticyclone over Scandinavia, feeding easterly winds across the North Sea.

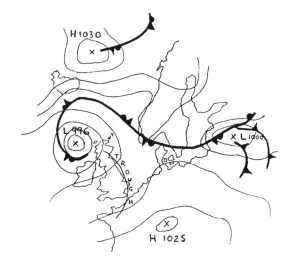

Simplified synoptic chart for 06.00 GMT on 21 May 1996. A depression to the west of Scotland, high pressure over Scandinavia and an occluded front stretching from the Baltic region resulted in several days of south-easterly winds, which brought many migrants from the Continent and Scandinavia.

Drift migration, exciting though it is to the expectant bird-watcher, is but a transitory and unpredictable phenomenon. Sutherland enjoys other, more regular, passages of migrants in spring and autumn, most of which are large scale and follow predetermined routes. The physical map of the county shows obvious flight lines, the most marked of which is the 'fault' running north-west from the Dornoch Firth to the north-west coast at Loch Laxford, via Loch Shin. This is used by Pink-footed Geese, some waders and probably many other species. The north/south running valleys of Loch Hope, Strathnaver and Strath Halladale provide well defined routes to and from the north coast.

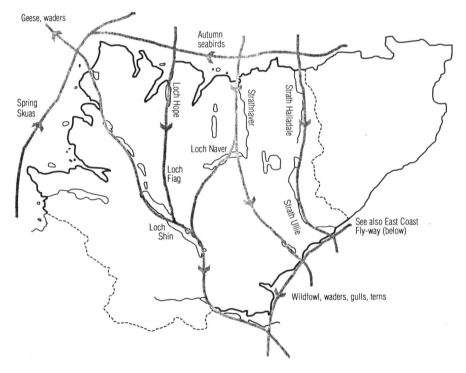

The east coast south of the Ord of Caithness is another major route. In autumn the preferred direction of flight for many diurnal migrants is south-west. A line drawn south-west from the eastern extremities of the Shetlands and Orkneys follows the east coast of Caithness and continues to Dornoch, at the south-eastern extremity of Sutherland, and ultimately through the Great Glen.

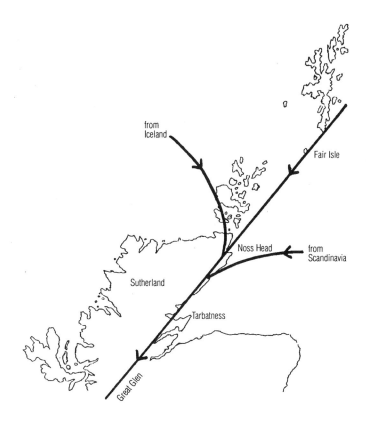

I live on this fly-way and sometimes see huge numbers of 'coasting' birds cutting off the 'Brora bump' as they head for Ben Bhraggie (Golspie) and beyond, including a British record count of Redwings in late October 1995 (see weather map on p. 119).

Migrating seabirds follow coasts and fathom lines. Although the Moray Firth is too shallow to attract deep water seabirds under normal conditions, it acts as a huge trap when strong easterly or south-easterly winds force them close inshore. Brora and Lothbeg Point are suitable vantage points to witness these movements, which sometimes involve thousands of birds. (See synoptic chart on p. 33).

On the north coast, the long promontories of Strathy Point and Faraid Head intercept seabirds, including many of the scarcer species, moving west through the Pentland Firth into autumn gales.

Winter Visitors

Sutherland's interior can be a harsh place in winter. A bird-watcher can walk all day in splendid surroundings and see only a handful of species. Ask anyone who's checked a random square for the BTO Winter Atlas!

The coasts are another world. Large numbers of divers and sea ducks take advantage of the rich waters of the Moray Firth. Species such as Long-tailed Duck sometimes number thousands. There are few places in Britain where flocks of a dozen or more Black-throated Divers can be encountered regularly. Parties of Great Northern Divers are more likely in the north, Loch Eriboll being the best locality. The main harbours usually attract the odd Glaucous or Iceland Gull. Onshore winds can drive in large numbers of Little Auks.

Winter is the best time to see Golden Eagles, at least in the south-east where prospective breeders have suffered persecution at the hands of some sheep farmers and unscrupulous gamekeepers as they try to establish new territories.

It may surprise a birder from the south to find that passerines such as Song Thrush, Skylark and Pied Wagtail are mainly summer visitors to Sutherland, but a good variety of resident species sees all but the harshest winter through, thanks partly to the efforts of members of the East Sutherland Bird Group who between them get through over ten tons of peanuts each year. Or rather their garden birds do! Flocks of Snow Buntings and Mealy Redpolls grace some winters. Most of the late autumn Redwings and Fieldfares normally move further south but small parties can appear at any time. One curiosity is the Blackcap. Sutherland lies at the northern limits of its British breeding range. Yet a small population spends the winter here, arriving in late autumn. Logic suggests they are breeders from the north of the range in Scandinavia, but it appears from ringing data that most are Continental birds which move north instead of south in winter.

A Typical Year

The title of this section is a contradiction in terms as one of the fascinations of bird-watching is that no two years are the same. Our birds are influenced by both local and, in the case of migrants, distant weather conditions. But some patterns do recur year on year.

By New Year most of the common northern visitors are settled in their winter quarters, although hard weather can bring new influxes of thrushes, sometimes accompanied by Waxwings, from Scandinavia and Russia. Golden Eagles are at their most prominent at this time, reaching the easternmost hills in their search for hares and grouse. The flocks of Greylags, a mixture of immigrants and local birds, are worth scanning for scarcer species, such as Greenland White-fronts. Flocks of Snow Buntings enliven coastal areas in the north and (mainly) hills in the south.

In the Moray Firth, a winter storm associated with a 'polar low' can produce a spectacular movement of auks. Numbers of Little Auks are unpredictable but prolonged onshore winds can result in sizeable 'wrecks' when dead or exhausted birds may be found well inland. Glaucous and Iceland Gulls can also occur in higher-than-usual numbers on such occasions. Very cold weather forces more vulnerable species, like the Stonechat, to beaches in search of tide-wrack insects.

By late February the first Skylarks have usually returned from their coastal wintering haunts to the south. The next arrivals, in mid March, are Song Thrushes from Ireland and the south-west and Lesser Black-backed Gulls. The first 'real' summer visitors – Wheatear and Sandwich Tern – can be expected, along with the odd Greenshank, at the very end of March, when Meadow Pipits return to the hills. Seabirds are now showing increasing interest in their cliff and island colonies. Puffins join the Razorbills and Guillemots after spending the winter far offshore. Sea-duck numbers build up dramatically in anticipation of their departure to northern breeding grounds. Rafts of Scoter in the Moray Firth are likely to include one or more Surf Scoters and many of the Long-tailed Ducks are in summer plumage. Slavonian Grebes can also be fairly numerous.

April can be a frustrating month in these northern latitudes. Expectations are high, yet the predominantly northerly airflow which has characterised several recent springs discourages all but the hardier summer migrants. It is mid month before Willow Warblers and hirundines appear, when large skeins of Pink-footed Geese move north-west. Most of the summer breeders are represented by the end of April although their numbers do not build up until early or even mid May. It is then that the traditional stragglers such as Spotted Flycatcher and Swift finally reach us.

Both May and June can produce the unexpected – perhaps a rare gull or wader, a migrant raptor, such as a Honey Buzzard or Marsh Harrier, a Scandinavian breeder like a Bluethroat blown west on easterly winds, or an exotic 'overshooter', such as a Bee-eater from southern Europe.

Breeding success is even more dependent on weather conditions in the far north than it is in southern Britain. A cool, wet summer can be disastrous for birds of prey, as well as for water birds and waders. The latter can be as much affected by rapidly fluctuating water levels as by cold and lack of food for their young. A North Atlantic high pressure system sometimes guarantees prolonged dry weather in May and June, particularly in the west, but the same conditions bring sea mists ('haar') to the east coast.

By July migrant waders are reappearing on the coasts and seabirds such as shearwaters and skuas become more numerous offshore. In two recent years large numbers of Long-tailed Skuas passed through the Moray Firth in August – possibly a phenomenon previously overlooked. Most of our breeding summer visitors leave quite early; September warblers may include migrants from elsewhere. A few Wheatears and hirundines continue to pass through in October.

The later autumn passage is the least predictable of the seasonal movements. The only certain thing is it will be exciting! Easterlies offer the prospect of seabird movements in the Moray Firth, sometimes including petrels and the rare shearwaters as well as skuas, and scarce migrants from as far as Siberia. North-westerlies promise spectacular flights of seabirds off the north coast. Late September sees major arrivals of ducks and geese from Greenland and Iceland, with Barnacles featuring mainly on the north and west coasts.

Large movements of Fieldfares and Redwings, and sometimes Bramblings, are typical of late October/November, when Pomarine Skuas harass the flocks of Kittiwakes offshore and Slavonian Grebe numbers peak in the south-east. Parties of Whooper Swans may linger briefly on their way south. Mealy Redpolls pass through in variable numbers in November and a few Waxwings can be expected, with larger irruptions in some years. Seabird movements can still feature the odd Sooty Shearwater at this time as well as Storm Petrel and Little Auk.

December is a good time to look for the rarer Arctic gulls in harbours. Iceland Gull numbers can reach double figures in good years. Wandering White-tailed Eagles are becoming a more regular sight thanks to the successful re-introduction programme in western Scotland. It takes quite a bird to make a Golden Eagle look puny! The optimist is ever on the lookout for a Snowy Owl or Gyr Falcon. More likely is a White-billed Diver or King Eider.

Where to Find Birds in Sutherland

Sutherland is blessed by such a wealth of wild terrain that it is possible to find good birds almost anywhere, but much of the hinterland and the higher tops are relatively inaccessible. This section highlights a few easily reached areas which, between them, offer the bird-watcher the opportunity to see most of the species for which the county is important.

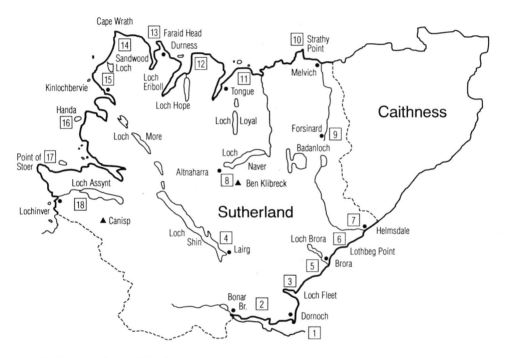

1. Dornoch and Embo
Divers, grebes, seaducks (winter and spring).
2. Migdale Woods and the Kyle of Sutherland
Woodland species, waterfowl.
3. Loch Fleet and The Mound
Wildfowl, waders, Osprey.
4. Lairg and Loch Shin (south)
Black-throated Diver (summer); winter and passage wildfowl.
5. Brora
Seabird passage, divers and seaducks (winter), gulls and terns, waders.

6. Lothbeg Point and Glen Loth
Seabirds (as Brora); Golden Eagle, Red Grouse, Dipper, Ring Ouzel.

7. Helmsdale
Iceland and Glaucous Gull (winter and spring).

8. Loch Naver and Ben Klibreck
Divers, Goosander, raptors, Ptarmigan, Greenshank, Dotterel.

9. Forsinard (RSPB)
Peatland specialities, raptors, Golden Plover. Information centre at railway station and peatland trails.

10. Strathy Point
Seabirds, wildfowl passage (mainly autumn) plus Scottish Primrose and cetaceans.

11. Kyle of Tongue
Seaducks, Greenshank, Arctic Tern; Barnacle Geese on offshore island (winter).

12. Loch Eriboll
Great Northern Diver and Slavonian Grebe (winter and spring), seaducks, raptors.

13. Durness area
Corncrake, Puffin, seabird and wildfowl passage, raptors, rare migrants.

14. Cape Wrath and Clo Mor
Huge seabird colonies (spring and summer).

15. Kinlochbervie and Sandwood Loch
White-winged Gulls, divers, Greenshank, Whooper Swans and geese (passage).

16. Handa Island (SWT)
Reserve open April-September. Seabird colonies (including Puffins); breeding Great and Arctic Skuas.

17. Stoerhead Lighthouse and Point of Stoer
Seabirds, Whimbrel (spring), Black Guillemot, cetaceans.

18. Loch Assynt area
Black-throated Diver, Golden Eagle, Ptarmigan, Dotterel, Snow Bunting.

Species List

This list includes all those species known to have occurred in Sutherland in the last two centuries. By the end of 1996 a total of 284 had been recorded. Of these 130 breed regularly in the county (a further 26 have done so on at least one occasion, 20 of them in the twentieth century, and four species, Great Northern Diver, Garganey, Water Rail and Turnstone, have almost certainly bred). Fifty-three are passage migrants, 27 are principally winter visitors and 68 are rare migrants or vagrants. To these must be added two recent re-introductions to the Highlands, Red Kite and White-tailed Eagle, and four species, Capercaillie, Nightjar, Chough and Corn Bunting, which can be regarded as more or less extinct in the county. Stock Dove and Tree Sparrow, now apparently both scarce migrants, and even Moorhen might soon join them. A further 11 species remain unverified and nine more were almost certainly escapes from captivity.

Most of the 18 new species recorded in the last 15 years are rare migrants, although there were some omissions from the list in *Sutherland Birds* (1983), such as Honey Buzzard and Chough (for which there were nineteenth-century records), and Black Redstart (first seen in 1978). Steller's Eider has been removed from the list as not proven. The 1953 record of Black-winged Stilt included in *Sutherland Birds* (1983) was excluded from *Birds in Scotland* (1986), but Harvie-Brown (1887) refers to a nineteenth-century specimen shot at Brora which perhaps merits its retention on the county list (even though it had been sold and could not be examined by Harvie-Brown).

In this book I have concentrated on the current status of species, including historical data mainly where significant changes have occurred. As far as the twentieth century is concerned, these are most noticeable in the species listed below, although the fortunes of some of these have fluctuated during that period. The status of many other species has changed to a lesser degree.

Breeding Birds in the Twentieth Century: Profit and Loss Account

Colonists	Tufted Duck, Goldeneye, Osprey, Whimbrel, Wood Sandpiper, Arctic Skua, Great Skua, Collared Dove, Redwing, Garden Warbler, Chiffchaff
Increase/ Expansion	Fulmar, Eider, Goosander, Hen Harrier, Buzzard, Oystercatcher, Woodcock, Black-headed Gull, G.B.B. Gull, Kittiwake, Guillemot, Razorbill, G.S. Woodpecker, Tree Pipit, Blackbird, Wood Warbler, Great Tit, Starling, House Sparrow, Goldfinch, Redpoll
Extinction	Capercaillie, Nightjar, Stock Dove, Tree Sparrow, Corn Bunting
Serious decline	Grey Partridge, Corncrake, Moorhen, Lapwing, L.B.B. Gull, Little Tern, Ring Ouzel, Magpie

The species list follows the order of Voous (1977). I have not adopted any of the new English bird names with the exception of Mediterranean Shearwater, which was only recently given specific status. (I prefer the name 'Balearic' Shearwater which, as I have argued elsewhere (Vittery, 1994), should be separated from the eastern Mediterranean 'Levant' Shearwater). My only departure from current taxonomic practice is to treat Arctic Redpoll as a race of Redpoll, in view of its apparently frequent hybridisation with the northward-expanding races of Greenland and Mealy Redpoll (Burton, 1995). Indeed, my own view is that if there is any justification for 'splitting' within this complex group, Lesser Redpoll is the best candidate.

Given the extreme local variation in the status of species in the county, and the fact that many of the scarcer migrants are undoubtedly under-recorded, I have decided not to ascribe arbitrary numerical connotations to terms of relative abundance, such as 'scarce' or 'common'.

Individual records within the species accounts are, with only a few exceptions, arranged on a calendar basis. Reference to a sighting in March 1996 would therefore precede one in April 1984.

In addition to data from published sources, the accounts include previously unpublished material from the files of successive County Recorders and some records from observers who do not use the normal channels. Where these involve British or Scottish rarities their 'unofficial' status is indicated by an asterisk, although their inclusion means I am fully satisfied with the identification.

I would welcome details of other unpublished observations for use in any future revision of this book. New records should be sent to the Recorder for the Highland region (which now includes Sutherland). At present (1997) this is Colin Crooke, c/o RSPB, Etive House, Beechwood Park, Inverness IV2 3BW (home address: 6 St George Street, Avoch, Easter Ross IV9 8PJ).

Red-throated Diver *Gavia stellata* (Breeding resident, passage migrant and winter visitor.)
By far the most numerous of the three divers occurring regularly in Sutherland. The breeding population appears to be fairly stable. The greatest density is found in the 'flows' of north/central Sutherland where the numerous small lochans provide ideal nesting sites.

Northward spring movements rarely reach major proportions: maximum 40 flying north-east off Brora on 15 April 1992. Off the north coast, there is a steady westerly passage in September/October. There were over one hundred on the sea between Embo and Dornoch in early October 1996 and 166 were counted there on 23 October 1982. On 12 November 1995, 71 flew north-east off Brora.

The wintering population is widely scattered around the coasts. Winter movements no doubt involve birds from outside our area. The largest recent passages are of 65 flying north-east at Brora on 13 December 1993 and 54 flying south there on 15 February 1995.

Black-throated Diver *Gavia arctica* (Scarce breeder, passage migrant and winter visitor.)
An RSPB census in 1996 found 53 pairs on territory in Sutherland – over 29% of the British population. This number should increase further through the use of artificial rafts for nesting, since flooding is the primary

cause of nest failure.

In spring, numbers build up in April, maxima 53 off Embo on 13 April 1995 and 24 there on 8 May 1994. Birds are also often seen on non-breeding lochs and there is some dispersal to such places in late summer, as well as to the coast.

Off Brora, there is some northward movement in autumn, maxima 7 on 4 October 1995, 5 on 21 October 1993 and 5 on 29 October 1992.

Concentrations occur in the south-east, with at least 40 between Loch Fleet and Dornoch on 30 October 1993.

Winter flocks are found mainly in the extreme south-east from the mouth of Loch Fleet to Dornoch, where parties of up to 14 have occurred in December/January.

Great Northern Diver *Gavia immer* (Winter visitor and passage migrant; may have bred.)
Harvie-Brown (1868) found a pair in Assynt in 1868 which appeared to be breeding. (The species nested in Wester Ross in 1970 and has been suspected to do so in Scotland on other occasions.) Summering birds are occasionally encountered, mainly in the north and west. An adult and two immatures were at Loch Fleet on 11 July 1988 and two flew south off

Brora on 12 July 1995.

In autumn the first birds arrive on the north coast in late August. The main arrival is in October/November, when there is a steady passage, mainly to the west, off the north coast (e.g. nine off Strathy Point on 4 October 1996). The largest numbers are usually in the north (maximum 41 in Loch Eriboll on 15 December 1995). Eleven flew north-east off Lothbeg Point on 13 October 1996.

Winter residents are widely scattered around the coasts. Eight flew north off Brora in a large diver movement on 13 December 1993.

Numbers build up before the spring departure, maxima 13 flying north off Brora on 23 April 1995 and 10 on the sea there on 6 May 1993. There were still five in Balnakeil Bay on 14 June 1993.

White-billed Diver *Gavia adamsii* (Rare winter visitor, but may occur more frequently than the records suggest.)
The three pre-1982 records were all between February and early April. Since then there have been a further four accepted sightings: one off Embo on 19 January 1995, one in Melvich bay on 7 August 1987, one found dead at Kinlochbervie on 25 August 1983 and one off Stoer Head on 6 November 1993. In addition an adult flew east off Strathy Point on 22 November 1995*.

Little Grebe *Tachybaptus ruficollis* (Scarce breeding resident.)
In the breeding season the species is confined to the few lochs and water-ways with fairly luxuriant fringing vegetation. The total population is unlikely to be much in excess of twenty pairs.

Although birds are more dispersed in winter and are sometimes seen on coasts, the small numbers involved do not suggest any significant immi-gration. One at Loch Sallachie, Bettyhill, on 7 April 1996 may have been a migrant.

Great Crested Grebe *Podiceps cristatus* (Scarce winter visitor and passage migrant.)
Since 1982, which was a good year with one on Loch Migdale on 3 May and up to three at Embo in November, the species has been reported in

only four years: one in the Dornoch Firth on 1 March 1983, one at Loch Fleet on 1 April 1993, one at Brora from 14-16 January, up to two at Embo from 15 January-19 March 1995 (one of which was probably the Brora bird), one flying north off Loch Fleet on 9 January and one in Helmsdale harbour on 26 February 1996.

Red-necked Grebe *Podiceps grisegena* (Scarce passage migrant and winter visitor. Recent summer record from the north.)
Two on the sea in Achmelvich Bay on 11 April 1996 (one remaining until 13th) were in summer plumage. Four off Golspie on 15 April 1994 is the largest spring count. One on Loch Brora in April 1996 is the only inland record.

One at Loch Eriboll on 25 June 1993 reflects the trend towards increased summering in Scotland and the species' recent breeding attempts in England.

The earliest autumn record is of a juvenile flying north at Lothbeg Point on 20 September 1994. Single passage birds have been seen off Brora, Embo and Dornoch between 24 September and 15 November.

Winter numbers are usually very small, with most birds off Embo/Dornoch.

Slavonian Grebe *Podiceps auritus* (Former breeder, passage migrant and winter visitor in small to moderate numbers.)
Following the colonisation of Inverness-shire in the early twentieth century, breeding occurred in Sutherland in 1929 and continued sporadically until the 1960s. There are no confirmed reports in recent years although one or two birds were present at an inland loch in the early 1980s.

The largest spring counts are off Embo/Dornoch in spring and autumn, maxima 65 on 1 April 1993, and 1989 on 15 April 1994. A few also occur in the north-west, in Balnakeil Bay and the Kyle of Tongue, in late March/April and two were seen from Handa Island on 23 April 1984. Small numbers linger into early May. Two off Dornoch on 8 July 1992 and a juvenile off Brora on 6 August 1996 are the only recent summer records.

In autumn, birds are noted from early October. There were 73 off

Embo/Dornoch on 30 October 1993 and 87 on 19 November 1994. Even at favoured localities, numbers fluctuate wildly in response to wind and tidal conditions. Two flying south off Brora on 23 October 1995 is the only evidence of coastal movement.

Mid-winter numbers in the south-east are normally fairly small, maximum 21 off Dornoch in mid-December 1996. Up to five have been seen in Loch Eriboll in January/February.

Black-necked Grebe *Podiceps nigricollis* (Rare winter visitor and passage migrant.)
Prior to 1982 this elusive species occurred occasionally off Embo/Dornoch in winter. The only recent record there is of one on 1 November 1993 but one flew north-east at Lothbeg Point on 18 December 1996. In the west, one was seen at Stoer in August 1962.

Fulmar *Fulmarus glacialis* (Common breeding resident and passage migrant.)
Disperses at sea but is away from breeding areas for only a short period in winter.

The spectacular rise in the population of this species during the twentieth century, and its corresponding geographical spread (including the occupation of inland sites), is well documented. The rate of increase in the population now appears to be slowing. The largest Sutherland colonies are in the north and west, with several thousand pairs on the cliffs at Clo Mor and on Handa. The largest inland colony is at Carrol Rock, Loch Brora, which has several hundred pairs, and smaller numbers nest as far inland as Rogart. A 'blue phase' bird with a 'normal' mate has occupied a site by the River Brora since at least 1992 and another has returned to Puffin Bay, Handa, several years running.

At least 8400 passed Faraid Head in just two hours on 22 February 1994. Autumn movements off the north coast (flying west) and the east coast (flying north/north-east) sometimes exceed 1000 birds per hour. An estimated 20,000 passed Strathy Point on 27 August 1995. Off Brora, there was a particularly heavy passage in early autumn 1993, increasing from about 1000 per hour on 3 September to 2000 per hour on 9 September. A pure albino flew north on 11 September 1993, presumably

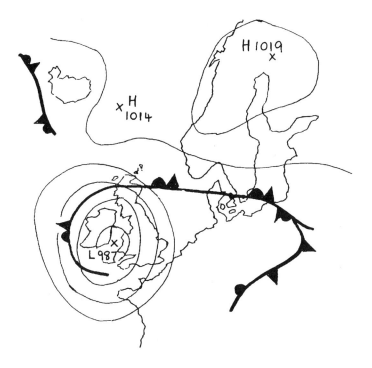

Simplified synoptic chart for 12.00 GMT on 9 September 1993. The combination of a depression over Ireland and an occluded front across Scotland and the North Sea caused a spectacular movement of seabirds in the Moray Firth featuring Sooty, Great and 'Balearic' Shearwaters, Leach's Petrel, Pomarine Skuas and many thousands of Fulmars.

the bird reported off North Norfolk and the Farne Islands during the preceding few days and again off Brora on 10 August 1996.

In addition to the breeding 'blue phase' individual mentioned above (which has got slightly paler with age), birds of varying degrees of darkness are seen fairly often. 'Double-dark' birds flew north off Brora on 19 April 1993, 9 August 1994, 26 August 1995 and 11 November 1995 and a medium-dark type passed there on 17 June 1993. The large Fulmar passage on 9 September 1993 (see above) included at least ten 'blue phase'.

Cory's Shearwater *Calonectris diomedea* (Scarce passage migrant, mainly in late summer and autumn.)
Possibly as a result of the warming of the North Atlantic and northern North Sea, this unmistakable large shearwater is now a more or less annual visitor to Sutherland waters in small numbers.

There have been the following sightings of single birds off the east, north and west coasts, all between June and September: off Golspie on 1 June 1983, flying north off Brora on 26 July 1995 and 3 August 1994, flying west off Faraid Head on 25 August 1995 and Strathy Point on 29 August 1993, flying north off Loch Fleet on 30 August 1979 and off Brora on 7 September 1993, 8 September 1995 and 26 September 1976.

Great Shearwater *Puffinus gravis* (Scarce passage migrant, mainly in autumn.)
Prior to 1982 there were just three records: one off Eilean nan Ron on 10 August 1962, one flying south off Handa on 1 September 1973 and two flying north off Brora on 26 September 1976. Since then, one flew south-west off Brora on 30 May 1996 (ahead of a severe gale in the eastern Atlantic), one flew west off Faraid Head on 25 August 1995, one flew north-west off Strathy Point on 10 September 1996 and singles flew north-east off Brora on 9/10 September 1993 and 13/14 October 1991, and off Lothbeg Point on 13 October 1996.

Sooty Shearwater *Puffinus griseus* (Autumn passage migrant, usually in moderate numbers, but commoner in good years.)
Sooty Shearwaters breed from the South Atlantic to the Antipodes and perform an incredible figure-of-eight migration each year which brings them into the eastern Atlantic and North Sea in late summer and autumn. The earliest was at Brora on 11 July 1995. Larger counts are usually from the second half of August to early October (late October in 1995). A few birds linger into November. Exceptionally, eight flew north-east off Brora on 11 November 1995 and two more passed on 26th.

There have been no recent passages to match that of 26 September 1976 when 430 flew north-east off Brora in an hour. Eighty passed in an hour on 22 September 1996 including a flock of 50 and 100 passed in

105 minutes on 1 October 1993. Off the north coast there is a more steady westerly passage in autumn of 5-10 per hour in 'normal' weather conditions. Larger movements occur in north-westerly winds, maxima 259 (in eight hours) off Strathy Point on 10 September 1996 and 250 in under four hours the following day.

Manx Shearwater *Puffinus puffinus* (Non-breeding summer visitor and passage migrant. Rare in winter.)
The largest numbers normally occur off the west and north coasts, nearest the species' principal British breeding colony on Rum. In spring the first birds normally appear from about late March (earliest 28th off the east coast). A westward passage of 327 per hour at Faraid Head on 15 April 1972 has not been bettered in recent years.

Passage and/or feeding flights continue through the spring and summer. Numbers in the Moray Firth are normally relatively small but 102 flew north off Brora on the evening of 22 May 1996 and over 100 flew south off Embo on 27 May 1986. Peak numbers normally occur in July/August. There was a heavy passage off Brora from 8-12 July 1995, with between 100 and 300 per hour in the evenings, and 418 flew north there on 5 August 1996.

Off the north coast, around 20 per hour is a normal rate of passage in late summer/early autumn. On 27 August 1995, 155 flew west off Strathy Point. Similar numbers can occur there and off the east coast in September but no more than 30 have been seen in a day in October. A few linger into November.

Singles flying north off Lothbeg Point on 18 December 1996 and Brora on 22 December 1995 were unusually late.

Mediterranean (Balearic) Shearwater *Puffinus (yelkouan) mauretanicus* (Scarce autumn passage migrant.)
There have been nine records since 1984: two between 26-29 July (Brora and Handa), three in the second half of August (Handa (two) and Faraid Head) and two on 9/10 September (Brora and Strathy Point, the latter feeding with Fulmars just offshore in 1996). Singles flew north-east off Brora on 1 October 1993 and off Lothbeg Point on 13 October 1996.

Little Shearwater *Puffinus assimilis* (Vagrant from the Atlantic.)
This species, like Mediterranean and Cory's Shearwater, has been occurring more frequently in northern waters and might prove to be a scarce, but regular, migrant if sea temperatures continue to rise. One flew north at Brora, very close in, on 21 October 1994 during a large seabird movement. One was also reported off Handa on 20 August 1993. This species is routinely rejected by the British Birds Records Committee, so its status in Sutherland remains 'unofficial'.

Storm Petrel *Hydrobates pelagicus* (Breeding summer visitor and passage migrant.)
One off Brora on 20 April 1993 was the earliest. A census of the northern islets in 1995 revealed between 163 and 230 adults on site on Eilean nan Ron, 56-79 on Eilean Losal, 31-44 on Eilean Hoan and 4-7 on the Rabbit Islands. On Eilean nan Roan, 293 were trapped on 25/26 July 1992, including one with a Norwegian ring. Trapping at Strathy Point in July/August 1994 demonstrated much interchange with the Northern Isles. One caught on 20 July 1994 had been ringed at Flo, Ulstein,

Norway on 10 August 1993. The most southerly recovery of a Sutherland-ringed bird was off the Moroccan coast.

Away from the breeding colonies the species is most frequently seen from Handa (June-September). In a north-westerly gale there on 16 August 1990 at least 1500 passed offshore. Three were seen in the Kyle of Durness on 19 September 1990. Elsewhere it is only infrequently seen on sea-watches, mainly in the north, but seven flew north-east off Lothbeg Point on 13 October 96. In 1991 there were unusual numbers in the Moray Firth: a total of 41 was seen off Brora between 17 and 19 October and eight more on 31 October. In 1995, two flew north-east at Lothbeg Point on 12 November, one flew north-east at Brora on 25 December and another passed Lothbeg Point on 1 January 1996.

Leach's Petrel *Oceanodroma leucorhoa* (Scarce passage migrant, mainly in autumn.)
The only spring records are of single birds flying east/north-east off Brora on 19 April and 30 May 1993 (both in heavy rain). Five were trapped on Leac Buidhe on 5 July 1990 and three at Strathy Point on 5 August 1985.

The species appears to be fairly regular in autumn off the north coast. At Strathy Point, there are nine recent records of birds flying west between 27 August and 20 October, all singles apart from two on 28 September 1996, two on 7 October 1996 and eight on 20 October 1995. One was blown into the Kyle of Durness on 19 September 1990. Off the east coast, one flew north-east at Brora on 9 September 1993 and one passed Lothbeg Point on 13 October 1996. One at Achfary on 16 November 1971 is both the latest date and the most recent inland sighting.

Gannet *Sula bassana* (Common non-breeding summer visitor and passage migrant; scarce from early January to mid March.)
Still increasing as a breeding bird in Britain, the species has recently established a colony on the south side of the Moray Firth and up to 20 were ashore at Am Balg (off Sandwood Bay) in summer 1996 – a possible prelude to nesting. Numbers increase in April as adult birds return to northern breeding colonies. There were over 400 off Handa on 26 May 1984 and up to 500 have been seen there in June.

Gannets off Brora, 1990-96

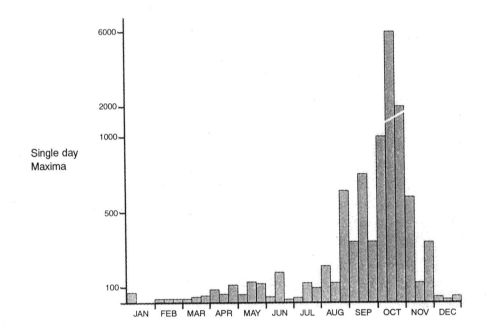

Single day Maxima

Large feeding flocks may be seen off any coast in late summer/autumn. Unusually, at least 200 were plunging into the breakers just off Brora beach on 8 October 1995.

The biggest movements are associated with autumn gales. There were 2500 off Handa on 16 August 1990, with 1700 the following day. Over 1000 flew west off Strathy Point on 27 August 1995 and birds were passing at about 600 per hour there on 27 September 1994. At least 1000 flew north-east off Brora on 2 October 1994 (mainly first year birds), 10 and 12 October 1991 and 19 October 1994, with at least 6000 there on 13 October 1996, 3500 on 18 October 1991and 1500 on 24 October 1995. November totals are much lower but over 600 flew north-east off Brora on 3 November 1995. Thirty-two off Brora on 25 December 1995 is the largest winter count.

Cormorant *Phalacrocorax carbo* (Resident breeder and passage migrant.) Several hundred pairs probably nest around Sutherland's coasts, mainly in the west. Many of the birds from the large Caithness colonies feed in the Moray Firth off the Sutherland coast. Although often seen on inland lochs, none appears to breed.

Disperses widely outside the breeding season. In autumn, numbers are augmented by arrivals from the Northern Isles, many of which probably pass further south.

The largest concentrations are found in the extreme south-east: up to 70 at Dornoch (February and October) and up to 50 at Brora (May) and Loch Fleet (autumn/winter).

Shag *Phalacrocora aristotelis* (Abundant breeding resident.)
Although the numbers of this species are subject to large (and often inexplicable) fluctuations, the 'normal' breeding population of Sutherland is thought to be between 2-3000 pairs, mainly in the north and west. A census on Handa in 1995 revealed a 67% decline from the 1987 population. Large numbers feeding in the Moray Firth probably include many from the Caithness colonies to the north.

Such movements as there are probably result mainly from feeding conditions. Off Brora, birds were moving north at 120 per hour on 7 September 1995 but several hundreds per hour were flying south there on 15 October 1995. An estimated 5000 flew south off Helmsdale in just half an hour on 10 October 1996.

Other recent large counts include: 500 off Brora in January/February 1991; several hundreds there on 30 June 1993; up to 800 in Handa Sound in late August 1985, over 1000 at Lothbeg Point on 22 December 1991 and 1000 off Point of Stoer on 22 December 1996.

Bittern *Botaurus stellaris* (Former breeder; now a rare winter visitor.)
Bitterns could be heard booming in Sutherland until at least the mid nineteenth century. There have been no recent records and only two in the twentieth century: at Loch Eriboll on 20 February 1936 and at Dornoch on 13 December 1954.

Little Bittern *Ixobrychus minutus* (Vagrant from southern Europe.)
A male on Handa on 8 May 1995 was found dead the following day.

Little Egret *Egretta garzetta* (Vagrant from Europe, but may be expected to occur more freqently in future given the numbers now present annually in southern Britain.)

One at Bonar Bridge on 22 June 1954 is the only record.

Grey Heron *Ardea cinerea* (Breeding resident.)

The number of breeding pairs in Sutherland is difficult to estimate as there is a scattering of small colonies or single nests on the relatively inaccessible west coast. The present population is certainly rather higher than the 33 pairs found during a national census in 1954 and is probably between 50 and 80 pairs.

Of the larger tree colonies, there were nine occupied nests at Altnaharra in 1988 and 27 at Clashmore in 1993. The latter has translocated to Skibo, where there were 34 pairs in 1996.

Post-breeding concentrations of up to 25 birds assemble at Loch Fleet. Up to 15 have been seen in the Kyle of Tongue in autumn. Small numbers of presumed migrants have been seen following the east coast fly-way in March and August/September. Winter numbers may be augmented by a few arrivals from Scandinavia.

Photographs of a pure white heron taken at Golspie in 1994 appear to be of an albino Grey Heron.

[Purple Heron] *Ardea purpurea* (Possible vagrant from Europe.)

One was reported from Loch Hope on 4 June 1986 (a very likely date for a southern 'overshooter') but the record was not accepted as proven.

Black Stork *Ciconia nigra* (Vagrant from south-eastern Europe.)

One at Loch Brora on 18 May 1977 is the only record.

White Stork *Ciconia ciconia* (Vagrant from Europe.)

There were four occurrences of single birds in the 1970s, all between 17 April and 20 May. Since then, the only record is of an adult at Helmsdale on 19 October 1996, which flew south-west through the Clynelish valley, Brora, the following day. (It arrived on the Black Isle, Easter Ross, that afternoon, where it remained well into November.)

Glossy Ibis *Plegadis falcinellus* (Vagrant from southern Europe.)
One at Cambusavie, Dornoch on 3 December 1962 is the only record.

Spoonbill *Platalea leucorodia* (Vagrant from Europe.)
An immature remained at Loch Fleet from 7 December 1975 until 20 January 1976.

[Chilean Flamingo] *Phoenicopterus chilensis* (Escape.)
A number of escaped Flamingoes are at large in Britain. The only one to have reached Sutherland so far spent the autumn of 1976 on the Dornoch mudflats. Presumably the same bird appeared at Bettyhill in March 1977.

Mute Swan *Cygnus olor* (Breeding resident.)
The only sizeable numbers occur in the extreme south-east, around the Dornoch Firth and the Kyle of Sutherland. The breeding population is small but fairly stable at around 30-40 pairs. Loch Brora is the northern-most regular breeding site but has only one pair. A pair also occasionally nests near Lairg. Post-breeding concentrations of up to 150 birds occur at the Kyle of Sutherland (Loch Maikle).

Three arrived from the south off Brora on 7 October 1994 and settled on the sea. The largest winter count is of 132 at Loch Maikle on 17 February 1991. A few sometimes winter in Loch Fleet. The species is rare in the west and north. There was one at Kinlochbervie on 4 May 1991.

Bewick's Swan *Cygnus columbianus* (Vagrant.)
This species is long overdue, having last been positively identified at Altnaharra in 1879! The much larger numbers wintering in Scotland since the 1970s give cause for optimism.

Whooper Swan *Cygnus cygnus* (Passage migrant and winter visitor; a potential breeder.)
There are no breeding records although a pair stayed at Loch Hope through the spring of 1990 and there were singles at Melvich on 13 June 1986 and Handa on 14 June 1990.

Most records are now of birds passing through in spring and autumn but a few overwinter or re-appear in mid winter. Some 'traditional' wintering sites, such as the fields south of Golspie, are no longer used.

Autumn arrivals usually commence in October. One at the Kyle of Sutherland on 15 September 1995 and a small flock on the Dornoch Firth on 24 September 1994 are the earliest records in recent years. Flocks arriving at the Kyle of Durness in October can provide a memorable spectacle and 77 came in at Strathy Point as late as 30 November 1988. Small parties flying north-east over the sea off Brora from October to December are presumably returning to Caithness wintering grounds.

The largest recent winter counts are of 51 in the Loch Evelix area on 16 December 1990 and 25 (all adults) at Loch Fleet on 24 December 1985. A total of 30 birds was seen at four sites in the west and north-west on 22 February 1991.

In spring most birds presumably overfly to the west. Flocks of 13 at Loch Brora on 1 April 1996 and Loch Buidhe on 7 April 1992 are typical in the east. Sixteen flew north-east over the sea off Brora on 2 April 1991. Stragglers occur into May, such as two at Melvich on 15 May 1986 and one at Loch Croispol on 27 May 1991.

[Black Swan] *Cygnus atratus* (Escape.)
Several feral birds are at large in the Highlands. One joined the Mute Swans on Loch Maikle, Kyle of Sutherland, in May 96.

Bean Goose *Anser fabalis* (Rare winter visitor and passage migrant.)
Up to the end of the nineteenth century Bean Geese were common in Scotland but there is no indication that they were anything but scarce in Sutherland.

Four of the five records have been since 1993: one south of Golspie on 31 January 1993, one arriving from the north-east at Brora on 27 February 1993, one at Skibo, Loch Fleet, on 10 March 1977, another coming in from the north-east at Brora on 8 October 1995 and one flying south-east over the River Brora, calling, on 17 October 1996.

Pink-footed Goose *Anser brachyrhynchus* (Passage migrant, with larger numbers in spring.)

The increase in the size of the British wintering population is reflected in the numbers which now pass through Sutherland. With the exception of a few individuals which remain with wintering Greylags, Pink-feet move quickly through Sutherland in autumn on their way further south. Five at The Mound on 29 August 1989 were exceptionally early. The first birds normally arrive in mid September: 60 flew south off Brora on 12 September 1992 and 200 came in at Strathy Point on 17 September 1990. Passage continues until late October.

Winter numbers are normally very low but a flock of 33 flew south-west at Brora on 30 January 1993.

Birds begin moving north again in March but the main passage is in April. Up to 2500 were in the Dornoch area in the second week of April in both 1990 and 1991. Later that month the peak exodus occurs: thousands follow the 'north-west passage' from Bonar Bridge, via Loch Shin. At Handa, a count of 3605 was made between 14 April and 1 May 1990. About 300 flew west at Strathy on 4 May 1986. Stragglers include one at the Kyle of Tongue on 1 June 1994 and one on Handa from 12 June to 7 July 1982. One summered at The Mound in 1989.

White-fronted Goose *Anser albifrons* (Scarce winter visitor and passage migrant.)
All records refer to the Greenland race *A. a. flavirostris* unless stated.

A flock of 23 passed Strathy Point early on 28 September 1996 and 25 followed on 1 October 1996, all heading south-east, straight for their Caithness wintering grounds. Most of the Caithness arrivals from Greenland (via Iceland) probably pass within sight of the north Sutherland coast. On 4 October 1996, at the same locality, a flock of 15 came south-west across the Pentland Firth from Hoy and turned west. These were presumably birds from one of the west coast wintering grounds. Two flocks totalling 44 birds came in at Durness on 25 October 1987.

In the south-east, there were eight near Loch Evelix on 20 October 1996, five came in at Embo on 3 November 1993, three were seen at Skibo on 4 November 1986 and nine at Loch Ospisdale on 16 November 1986 (two remaining into December).

Very small numbers occur in the south-east in most winters. Up to five over-wintered at Pulrossie in 1995/96. Two immatures at Brora on 27 December 1995 were of the nominate race, reflecting a mini-invasion of 'Eurasian' birds in Scotland that winter.

There are two records of spring passage flocks: 50 over Brora on 4 April 1992 and 200 were seen at Loch Truderscraig on 5 May 1979.

Greylag Goose *Anser anser* (Breeding resident, passage migrant and common winter visitor.)
Recent studies of marked birds have shown the movements of this species, within and outwith our area, to be even more complex than previously thought. This is partly a result of the widely differing origins of the birds occurring in Sutherland. The original indigenous population has become increasingly 'polluted' by feral populations (albeit of Hebridean stock) which are well established, and increasing, in the south-east. Mixing occurs both at winter feeding sites and at the summer moult, the main location of which has moved from Badanloch to Loch Loyal. The resident birds are joined in winter by immigrants from Iceland, some of which pass on to the south or return to Caithness.

The scattered nature of the breeding population, in difficult terrain, makes any estimate of its current size guesswork. Feral breeders in the south-east certainly now number more than 200 pairs. Birds recommenced breeding in the Badcall Bay area in the early 1990s after a lapse of many years and there were eight broods on Loch Laxford in 1996, suggesting some expansion in the west. The first broods are usually in evidence in mid May (earliest 5 May 1993 at Clynelish Moss). On 2 July 1992 1437 moulting birds were on Loch Loyal.

The main spring passage is in April. In April 1982, 2114 flew northwest over Handa, over 1000 passed Brora on 20 April 1992 and 2500 flew north-west at Bonar Bridge on 21 April 1985 – an indication of the importance of the Kyle of Sutherland/Loch Shin as a spring departure route. Only small numbers straggle into May.

The first returnees arrive in September. Twenty-five came in at Brora on 9 September 1992 and 250 arrived at Melvich on 15 September 1982. Numbers then increase, with the main movements taking place in October. Birds were flying south off Brora at about 300 per hour on 16

October 1995 and there were 1860 at Loch Fleet on 29 October 1994, 1958 at Dornoch on 29 October 1989, 1100 at Loch Brora on 4 November 1993 and 4122 at Loch Ospisdale on 16 November 1986, where there were 2500 on 12 January 1986.

[Bar-headed Goose] *Anser indicus* (Feral/escape.)
Birds of unknown origin are being seen with increasing frequency in Britain. Two adults remained in the Golspie area for about three weeks in August 1993 and an adult at Altnaharra on 9 June 1996 transferred to Loch Ereacha, Melvich, where it spent the summer and autumn.

Snow Goose *Anser caerulescens* (Vagrant from North America/escape.)
There were five records (of six birds) between 1971 and 1981 – one in January, one in April, two in June and one in early July. In 1985 there was one in the Dornoch Firth in January/February and four at Skibo on 6 May, which left to the north-west. A singleton (possibly the 1985 bird) was seen at various locations in the south-east from 12 January to 9 March 1986 and again in November/December 1986, after being seen arriving with Greylags at Durness on 4 October .

[Emperor Goose] *Anser canagica* (Escape.)
Three were seen on Handa on 4 July 1984.

[Ross's Goose] *Anser rossii* (Probable escape.)
One was seen at Kinlochbervie on 30 May 1991.

Canada Goose *Branta canadensis* (Formerly rare; now scarce breeding resident and moult migrant, mainly in the extreme south.)
The evolution of a moult migration from Yorkshire (and perhaps else-where) to the Beauly Firth by this introduced species is well documented (e.g. Walker 1970). Overshooters from this movement probably originally accounted for most of the few birds seen in Sutherland prior to 1980, which were mainly confined to the inner Dornoch Firth and the Kyle in the extreme south. Recent breeding attempts and the presence of small winter flocks have now complicated the picture.

The species began to attain its present status in the mid 1980s and breeding was first proved in 1988. There were six pairs at Loch Ospisdale in 1995. Winter flocks were established by the early 1990s: up to 19 at Bonar Bridge/Kyle of Sutherland in February and a maximum of 22 there on 13 December 1992.

Elsewhere it is very rare. Two at Handa in May 1991and seven there on 7 June 1990 were presumably displaced moult migrants. One was seen at both the Kyle of Tongue and Melvich on 29 July 1975.

Barnacle Goose *Branta leucopsis* (Winter resident and passage migrant.) Two discrete populations visit or pass through Sutherland. Wintering birds from the Greenland population are restricted to islands off the north and west coasts (occasionally visiting the adjacent mainland). Their total number in any one year is less than 1000. Migrants from the Spitsbergen population are occasionally seen en route to the Solway Firth. Odd birds with goose flocks in the south-east are of suspect origin.

The earliest arrivals are in late September: 12 flew west at Strathy Point on 27 September 1994. There were already over 100 on Eilean Hoan on 3 October 1996. Eighty-five which flew south-west at Brora on 29 September 1994 and several hundreds between 12 and 14 October 1996 were presumably ex-Spitsbergen en route to Caerlaverock. There were 24 at Cuthill (Dornoch) on 27 October 1995, six remaining until 5 November.

Eilean Hoan, off the north coast, holds the largest number of wintering birds. A maximum of 734 on 30 October 1982 may have included some migrants but there were 556 on 14 January 1985. Up to 250 winter in smaller groups off the west coast. In 1982/83, 12 wintered at Bonar Bridge.

Spring passage is evident only in the extreme west. Handa witnesses small numbers, maximum 27 on 12 April 1982. Flocks of 13 and 14 flew north-west there on 1 and 3 May 1982 respectively and one was seen on 9 June 1993.

Brent Goose *Branta bernicla* (Scarce winter visitor and passage migrant.) Both the dark-bellied (*B. b. bernicla*) and light-bellied (*B .b. hrota*) forms occur in Sutherland – the former usually singly or in very small numbers; the latter sometimes in small flocks.

The earliest autumn record is of 17 (pale-bellied) at the Kyle of Tongue on 6 September 1981. A pale-bellied flew west at Strathy Point with Barnacle Geese on 27 September 1994. An immature at the Kyle of Tongue on 1 October 1988, 20 pale-bellied there on 5 October 1980, one pale-bellied at Littleferry on 11 October 1995, four flying south off Brora on 14 October 1991 and one at Pulrossie on 31 October 1995 are the only other recent autumn records.

In the nineteenth century Brent Geese were fairly common in winter but parties at this season are now scarce. There were four at Loch Fleet from 24-26 February 1956 and six (pale-bellied) at Embo from 19 January-7 February 1985. One wintered at Loch Fleet/Dornoch in 1979/80.

Spring passage commences in early March. Dark-bellied birds occurred at Loch Fleet from 4-7 March 1985, at Brora on 9 March 1993 and 12 March 1992, at Brora and Loch Brora from 22 March-1 April 1996 and off Brora (flying north) on 26 April 1992. There were two pale-bellied birds on Handa on 17 April 1995 and four at Dornoch on 8 May 1994.

Ruddy Shelduck *Tadorna ferruginea* (Formerly an irruptive vagrant from western Asia. No records this century.)
In 1892, five were seen at Durness on 20 June and further flocks of 10 and 14 occurred in late June and early July. The species now breeds ferally on the near Continent and occurs annually in southern Britain. Sadly, future sightings, while more likely, will no longer be determinable as 'pure'.

Shelduck *Tadorna tadorna* (Breeding resident on coasts. Adults are absent during the moult.)
Sutherland's breeding population is widely scattered around the coasts but the greatest concentration is in the south-east. About 20-25 pairs nest at Loch Fleet, where numbers peak at around 200 in mid July. The species is scarcest in the west although small numbers occur on Handa in most summers. Adults leave in August for their moulting grounds – either the Forth Estuary or the Heligoland Bight, returning late in the year.

Ten year winter maxima are around 180 at Loch Fleet and 150 at Dornoch. Winter numbers in the north are small. Thirty-three at the Kyle of Tongue on 2 April 1995 may have included prospective breeders moving up from the south.

Wigeon *Anas penelope* (Scarce breeder, passage migrant and abundant winter visitor.)

The small breeding population is well scattered from the south-east through the central and northern peatlands. NCC surveys in the 1980s indicated that the 'Flow Country' of Sutherland and Caithness held about 80 pairs (Ratcliffe and Oswald, 1988). It is reasonable to assume from this that the total Sutherland population is at least 60 pairs. One ringed at Loch Brora in June 1909 was recovered in the Netherlands that September (the first recovery of a Sutherland-ringed bird).

Numbers at Loch Fleet begin to build up in August. The main arrival is from mid September, e.g. 4200 at Dornoch on 17 September 1989, and the peak is usually in November/December. Although large autumn arrivals from Iceland are witnessed on the north coast, most of these birds are immigrants from the north-east. More than 1000 usually winter at Loch Fleet with several thousands in the Dornoch Firth. The main exodus takes place in March.

Smaller numbers winter on inland lochs and in northern sea lochs such as Loch Eriboll and the Kyle of Tongue. The species is scarcest in the west.

American Wigeon *Anas americana* (Vagrant from North America.)
A male at Loch Fleet on 2 July 1988 was probably the bird seen on at least three occasions there between October 1988 and February 1989. Another male was on Handa on 19 May 1990.

Gadwall *Anas strepera* (Very scarce breeder, passage migrant and winter visitor.)

Gadwall numbers have increased in the north of their range over the last 30 years, particularly in Iceland. The species was first proved to breed in Sutherland in 1913 and the odd pair has nested sporadically since. A pair nested successfully at a northern site in 1991 (five young), 1992 (six young) and again in 1995.

There was a male at the Kyle of Durness from 27 April-1 May 1985. The only autumn record is of a flock of 23 which flew south-east past Strathy Point on 1 October 1996 – a day of arrivals from Iceland.

There was a male at Skibo on 22 January 1984, where up to six have been seen in winter in the past.

Teal *Anas crecca* (Common breeding resident, passage migrant and winter visitor.)

The breeding population is widely but thinly distributed, getting scarcer to the west. NCC surveys in the 1980s showed it to be the most common species of wildfowl on the central and northern peatlands, being present on 75% of the sites visited.

Numbers at Loch Fleet build up in August. Small passage flocks are frequently seen off the north and east coasts in autumn. Immigrants are mainly of north-eastern origin.

The wintering population of around 2000 birds is confined to the south-east – mainly the Dornoch Firth and Loch Fleet, although good numbers feed inland on lochs and river systems, ice permitting.

Green-winged Teal *A. c. carolinensis* (Vagrant from North America.)
Males of this race occurred at The Mound on 30 April and 2 May 1995, Culrain on 7 June 1974 and at Loch Fleet from 23-31 December 1978.

Mallard *Anas platyrhynchos* (Common breeding resident and winter visitor.)

More widely distributed than other breeding wildfowl. Birds were present on two-thirds of the peatland sites surveyed by NCC in the 1980s. Breeding densities are highest in the south-east. For example, 20-30 pairs nest at Loch Fleet. Numbers are affected by releases for shooting and by winter immigrants, which arrive from late September onwards. At Loch Fleet 500 or more may be seen (maximum 900 on 27 January 1988) and the Dornoch Firth (744 on 19 October 1986). There were 357 in the Inner Dornoch Firth on 19 January 1992. As with other surface feeders, numbers in the north and west are comparatively small.

Pintail *Anas acuta* (Passage migrant and scarce winter visitor. May still be an occasional breeder in the north.)

There has been no proof of breeding in recent years but a pair was present at one south-central site in the early 1980s and there was a male at a former breeding site in the north in 1983. An apparent Pintail/Mallard hybrid was seen in the Dornoch Firth on 15 September 1996.

A regular autumn build up in the Dornoch Firth affords the only good opportunity to see the species in Sutherland. The first arrivals are in early September. Numbers then increase to an October peak of between 150 and 200 birds. Small flocks en route to this gathering fly south-west down the east coast in October (latest nine off Brora on 5 November 1995). In some years over 100 have remained until mid December but mid-winter numbers are very small. Exceptionally, there were still 25 at Dornoch on 20 January 1991.

A small but regular spring passage is evident at Loch Fleet between mid March and mid May. A flock of eight flew south-west at Brora on 25 April 1993.

Garganey *Anas querquedula* (Rare passage migrant; may have bred.)

A pair was present at a site in the south-east in 1992. Other pairs (all presumed 'overshooters') were seen at Achfary on 18/19 March 1996, Stoer on 10 May 1977 and Colaboll, Loch Shin in May 1991.

Blue-winged Teal *Anas discors* (Vagrant from North America.)

A male was seen at The Mound on 29 April 1993*.

Shoveler *Anas clypeata* (Scarce passage migrant and winter visitor. Has bred.)

Although breeding has not been proven this century, a pair was seen at Pollachpuill on 2 June 1988.

Apart from singles at Durness on 8 September 1987 (found dead) and Loch Fleet on 24 September 1986, the 1980s were blank years. Since 1991 there have been ten sightings of up to four birds in the south-east and north-west in January (one), February (two), April (one), late May (one), August (four records, including four birds near Durness on 4 August 1991) and October (one).

Red-crested Pochard *Netta rufina* (Vagrant from southern Europe.)
The only record is of a male in the Durness area on 26/27 May 1985.

Pochard *Aythya ferina* (Scarce passage migrant and winter visitor. Has bred.)
The species probably last nested in the 1970s. There are only three recent spring records: an immature male on Loch Brora on 21 March 1996, one flying north over the sea at Lothbeg Point on 12 April 1996 and five at Altnacealgach on 29 April 1986.

In autumn there are three records of birds flying north-east off Brora: singles on 15 September 1994 and 29 September 1992 and two on 23 October 1995. There were also two on Loch Brora on 7/8 October 1991.

Although good numbers winter in Caithness, Pochard do not find the acidic lochs of Sutherland to their liking. Lairg is the most favoured spot – up to 12 have been recorded there between late November and February. Elsewhere, three at Loch Migdale on 8 December 1983 is the largest number seen in recent years, apart from a flock of ten which flew south-west past Brora on 31 December 1995 after exceptionally cold weather had caused a large exodus from Scandinavia. One at Tongue on 14 January 1990 and two at Loch Caladail on 6 December 1993 are the only winter records from the north.

Ring-necked Duck *Aythya collaris* (Vagrant from North America.)
A male was seen intermittently at three lochs near Durness between 28 June 1977 and 7 November 1980.

Tufted Duck *Aythya fuligula* (Scarce breeder, mainly in the north-west, passage migrant and winter visitor.)
First proved to breed in 1935. The few breeding records in recent years suggest there may have been a decline from the 20 pairs estimated by Angus (1983). There were two pairs alarming near Whiteface in May 1994 and a female had five young at Durness on 30 June 1992. Eleven at Loch Borralie on 16 June 1990 may also indicate local breeding. In the south-east, a nest with six eggs near Dornoch in June 1974 was predated. A brood was seen at the same site on 24 July 1984. One or more pairs have bred at Loch Migdale in several years since 1986 and breeding was

suspected at Coul Links, Loch Fleet in 1988, where 13 (six males) in May declined to five in June. NCC surveys in the early 1980s indicate a few pairs may breed by remote lochans in the north-central peatlands.

Up to 12 at Loch Croispol (Durness) from 30 March-7 April 1991 may have been prospective breeders or spring migrants. A few passage birds are seen in the south-east in spring.

A small autumn passage off the coasts has been noted from late September to November: nine flew east off Strathy Point on 10 September 1996, eight flew west there on 28 September 1995 and up to three have passed Brora in mid October, where one flew south on 21 November 1993.

Winter numbers vary from year to year but are usually in the 100-200 range in the south-east. Flocks build up in September (40 in the Kyle of Sutherland on 15 September 1993) and peak in early winter (maximum 207 in the Kyle on 16 December 1990). Over a hundred have occurred on Loch Evelix and up to 24 at Lairg in January/February. In the north, 19 at Durness on 5 February 1985 is the largest winter flock.

Scaup *Aythya marila* (Scarce winter visitor and passage migrant. Has bred.) The last proven breeding was in 1899 (Baxter and Rintoul 1953). Single males were at Loch Eriboll on 29 May 96, at Melvich from 1-18 June 1988 and at Loch Fleet from 13-29 August 1985.

A small spring passage is evident, mainly between mid April and mid May. There were six on Loch Ospisdale on 29 May 1982. Autumn passage is also slight: two flew west off Strathy Point on 30 August 1996, two on 28 September 1995 and two on 21 October 1996 (presumably all en route to west coast wintering grounds). There were four at Embo, plus three in the Inner Dornoch Firth, on 11 October 1992.

The wintering flock in the Dornoch Firth prefers the Ross side. Up to 138 have crossed to Sutherland on occasions between late October and early March. Elsewhere, the species is surprisingly uncommon with only very small numbers appearing in some years at Loch Fleet. In winter 1994/95, a small flock built up at Dornoch, increasing to 40 in January/early February (five stayed until 12 March). Six flew north off Brora in very hard weather on 31 December 1995.

Eider *Somateria mollissima* (Breeding resident.)

The Eider is now such a characteristic bird of Sutherland's coasts it is hard to believe it did not breed in the county until the nineteenth century and not on the east coast until about 1915. The breeding population is well scattered along all coasts. One of the highest densities is at Loch Fleet, where up to 50 pairs have bred. Up to 20 pairs now nest on Handa, a slight decline on earlier years. A leucistic female, reared at Brora in 1992, remained in the natal area until early 1994.

Moulting flocks of up to 1100 birds were a regular sight in July/August off the mouth of Loch Fleet and Dornoch until the early 1990s but there has been a sharp decline in both these and in autumn numbers, which reached a maximum of 3500 in the early 1980s. In the north, there were 440 at Faraid Head on 14 October 1984, 500 at Strathy Point on 28 October 1984 and 208 in Loch Eriboll on 13 January 1985.

The wintering population in the south-east was very small in 1996/97.

King Eider *Somateria spectabilis* (Rare. Mainly winter visitor and spring migrant although at least one individual was semi-resident for several years.)

The species has been recorded only in the south-east, mainly in the Loch Fleet/Embo/Dornoch areas. No females have yet been identified (not just a result of their relative inconspicuousness – they are more reluctant than males to stray far from their breeding grounds). The first was seen on 17 November 1973 and was probably resident until September 1990. Two were present throughout 1979 and in April 1981 and March 1982. A second year male appeared in April 1988 with up to two adults, and there were also two or three in May/June 1989. In 1991 one was seen at Brora/Lothbeg Point between 28 March and 6 April. Presumably the same bird reappeared in late 1991, staying until early March 1992. It was not seen again at Brora until 24 December 1992, although one, possibly the same, was off Embo from 5-11 October 1992. In 1993 the Brora bird was present, intermittently, between 27 January and 19 March and again from 5-8 May. There have been no sightings since.

[Steller's Eider] *Polysticta stelleri* (Possible vagrant from Arctic Russia.) The authenticity of the female reported at Loch Fleet on 22 September 1959 is now doubted (Vaughan 1991).

Long-tailed Duck *Clangula hyemalis* (Common winter visitor; a potential breeder.)
This species has bred in the Northern Isles. A pair was displaying on a loch in the north-west in late spring 1984.

Two flew west at Strathy Point on 28 September 1996 and there were three off Brora on 29 September in 1994 but numbers do not build up until late October. Winter totals in the Moray Firth have declined from a peak of almost 7000 in 1983 to about 1000 by the mid 1990s. An area a few miles off Lothbeg Point now seems to be the preferred 'day roost'. The much smaller numbers off the north coast have shown a proportionate decline (40 in Balnakeil Bay in mid November 1991 is the highest recent total). The species is scarce on the west coast: there were three at Badcall on 3 November 1983, four at Handa on 21 November 1984 and one there on 8 April 1985.

In the south-east, northward passage has been noted off Brora in late March/April, maximum 462 on 30 March 1992. Numbers build up at

Embo/Loch Fleet in April, maximum 564 at Loch Fleet on 20 April 1988. Moderate numbers stay into May: there were still at least 350 at Embo on 4 May 1993, 37 flew north off Brora on 13 May 1993, with two on 18 May 1995. The occasional straggler has remained into June.

Common Scoter *Melanitta nigra* (Scarce breeder and common winter visitor.)
The remote northern peatlands of Sutherland and Caithness are the stronghold of the small British breeding population, accounting for more than half of the known pairs (fewer than 100). At least 18 pairs have nested in Sutherland in recent years.

The wintering population is confined to the south-east. Dornoch and Embo are the most favoured sites. As with the Long-tailed Duck, there has been a decline in recent years. Numbers peak in autumn (maximum 2500 at Embo on 2 October 1983) and spring (maxima 3900 on 7 March 1984 and 1500 on 1 May 1986), but in the 1990s no more than 500 birds were seen at either season.

Variable numbers of non-breeding birds summer, e.g. 50 off Loch Fleet on 28 June 1985 and 200 off Embo on 3 August 1986. A few are seen at Handa most summers.

There is surprisingly little evidence of coastal movement. Small spring departures and autumn arrivals have been noted at Brora but recent autumn sea-watches off Strathy Point produced only three sightings of up to four birds flying west between late August 1996 and early November.

Black Scoter *M. n. americana* (Vagrant from North America.)
A male of this distinctive North American race of the Common Scoter was seen off Dornoch and Embo on 15 April 1990. What was presumably the same bird reappeared on 23 March 1991 (staying until 2 May) and was again present from 6 March-4 April 1993.

Surf Scoter *Melanitta perspicillata* (Rare winter visitor and passage migrant, mainly in spring.)
First recorded at Loch Fleet on 21 March 1974, the species was seen off the south-east coast in seven winters up to 1984 with two males in

November/December 1976 and three on 28 April 1983. The only winter record since 1983/84 is of a male at Golspie on 24 February 1989. A male at Dornoch on 20 September 1992, a male at Embo between 27 September and 21 October 1984 and an immature at Loch Fleet on 16 October 1988, are the only autumn records.

Since 1991 it has been seen only in spring. There were two males and an immature off Embo in early May 1991. Two males reappeared in April 1992, one remaining until 13 May and there was a male at Brora from 22 April-17 May. On 27 April 1993 a pair was seen at Brora – the male extremely attentive. It is surely only a question of time before breeding is proved on this side of the Atlantic, presumably in the Baltic or further north-east. A male was seen at Dornoch on 1 and 3 March 1996.

The only two sightings in the west and north – at Handa in 1978 and Talmine (Tongue) in 1988 were both of males between 1-8 June.

Velvet Scoter *Melanitta fusca* (Winter visitor and passage migrant.)
Like several of the other sea-ducks, this species seems to have suffered a decline in recent years. The wintering population is centred on Embo and Dornoch and now usually numbers between 100 and 200 birds. There is a spring build-up to a late April/early May peak of up to 400. There are a few summer records. Autumn migrants/immigrants are noted from early September. Ten flew south-west at Brora on 18 September 1994.

Records elsewhere are sparse. There were three at Loch Shin on 9 May 1983 and a drake at Durness on 14 May 1994. Twenty were reported near Cape Wrath on 16 July 1982 (although confusion with moulting drake Eiders is possible at this time of year). Two at Badcall on 16 December 1984 is the only recent report from the west.

Goldeneye *Bucephala clangula* (Common winter visitor. Has bred in recent years.)
A very nervous female at Loch Syre in spring 1980 was the first indication of possible colonisation. Following the placing of nest boxes at the Kyle of Sutherland in the mid 1980s, five at Bonar Bridge on 2 July 1985 suggested possible local breeding. A female with ducklings was finally seen there in 1994 and again in the following two years. Males were present at

Loch Fleet on 4 June 1994 and 30 June 1985 and there was also one on Loch Brora on 30 June 1994.

This is the most widespread of the winter diving ducks, occurring on coasts, rivers, lochs and even small lochans, so far as icing allows. The largest concentrations in recent years have been in the Dornoch Firth area: 82 at Meikle Ferry on 21 October 1984, 93 in the Kyle of Sutherland on 16 December 1990 and 123 there on 17 February 1991. The biggest flock reported from the north was 29 at Loch Caladail on 6 December 1993. In the west, there were at least 35 in the Stoer area on 22 December 1996.

The earliest arrival was one flying south at Brora on 6 September 1992. In spring, most have departed by late April but a few straggle into May.

Smew *Mergus albellus* (Rare winter visitor and passage migrant.)
The six records are all of single birds between January and late April: one in January 1989, a male at Laxford on 24 February 1982, a 'redhead' at Lairg on 13 March 1989, a 'redhead' on Loch Brora on 18 March 1992, a male at Lairg from at least 23 March-8 April 1991 and another 'redhead' at Loch Brora on 24 April 1992.

Red-breasted Merganser *Mergus serrator* (Common breeding resident and winter visitor.)
Widely distributed, breeding on lochs, rivers and sea lochs. A female at The Mound on 13 July 1986 was in sole charge of exactly 50 ducklings!

Post-breeding concentrations of up to 150 birds are typical at Loch Fleet. There were 210 there on 24 September 1986 and 450 on 6 October 1984, by which time local residents have been joined by immigrants from Iceland. The largest flock recorded is 600 at Dornoch on 14 October 1984. There is some movement through the Pentland Firth in late September/October and 50 flew south-west at Brora on 11 November 1995.

Goosander *Mergus merganser* (Breeding resident in small numbers.)
This species was first proved to breed in Sutherland in 1875. Now, it is widely but sparsely distributed along the larger rivers. A density of one or two pairs per 10 miles (16 km) of river was estimated in the 1970s

(Sharrock, 1986). There may have been some decline from this figure but the species now appears to be holding its own despite continuing persecution by fisheries interests.

The bulk of Sutherland's breeders may join the main Highland concentration of wintering birds in the Beauly Firth but flocks are sometimes seen in the Kyle of Sutherland, e.g. 54 on 12 November 1982 and 52 on 14 December 1986. There were several males in Assynt in late December 1996 and near Melvich in January 1997.

Honey Buzzard *Pernis apivorus* (Rare summer visitor (becoming more regular) and passage migrant.)
Although not included in *Sutherland Birds* (1983), Harvie-Brown and Buckley (1887) knew the Honey Buzzard to be a rare autumn migrant in the nineteenth century. The increased incidence of this species in Scotland in the last 20 years is reflected in Sutherland. The first recent sightings were in the north in 1982. None was then seen until 1989 but since 1992 it has been an almost annual visitor.

The earliest record is of a pale-phase bird flying south-west through the Clynelish valley, Brora on 28 April 1992 – the standard flight line for 'overshooters' reorientating from the Northern Isles. There are reports of three, possibly four, individuals between 12 and 17 May (one in the north and two or three in the south-east) and another five records occur between 30 May and 14 June. The latest sightings are on 21 and 24 July, although birds of Scandinavian origin must still pass through in autumn occasionally.

Black Kite *Milvus migrans* (Rare passage migrant.)
This species has been increasing on the Continent and appearing in greater numbers in Britain in recent years. One was reported near Ben Griam on 23 May 1994* and another from Syre in late spring 1995*. After a period of very strong south to south-west winds had brought a number of southern raptors, including several Black Kites, to northern Scotland, one appeared in the Clynelish valley, Brora on the evening of 4 June 1996 and roosted in a small plantation on Clynelish Muir. Early next morning it flew off towards Loch Brora. Another (or perhaps the same) was reported from the Borgie Forest in July 1996*.

Red Kite *Milvus milvus* (Former breeder but extinct in the county by the early nineteenth century; re-introduced into the Highlands.)

Angus (1983) unfortunately perpetuated the myth that the species bred in Sutherland until 1860, an error already corrected by Pennie (1962). Naturally, only a vagrant this century but re-introduced birds are now appearing with increasing regularity. With luck (and tolerance!) the species will soon regain its former status.

One at Scourie on 19 March 1969 is the only 'genuine' migrant known to have occurred in recent times.

The first released bird to reach Sutherland was seen near Golspie on 5 October 1991. This may have been the individual which subsequently wintered in Strath Brora, staying until early March. From 1993 there have been several reports annually of birds in both the south-east and north-west. How long will we wait for a breeding pair?

White-tailed Eagle *Haliaeetus albicilla* (Former breeder (until 1901) and once commoner than Golden Eagle. Birds from the Scottish re-introduction programme are now being seen with increasing frequency.)

The first recent record was of one at Bettyhill on 27 April 1980. Since then there has been an adult at Ichnadamph on 14 April 1982, an immature at Drumbeg in 1990, an immature (untagged) near Brora on 7/8 October 1991, an immature on Handa on three occasions between 12 April and 2 May 1993, four sightings in 1994 (including one circling with a birder-piloted hang glider over Ben Bhraggie in July!) and several more in 1995/96.

Marsh Harrier *Circus aeruginosus* (Rare spring passage migrant, likely to become more frequent.)

Not recorded in the county until 1988. The increase in the size of north European populations and the northward spread of this species in the last 30 years account for the five recent records, three of which were on 9/10 May: a female west of Lairg on 9 April 1992, an immature female at Clynelish, Brora on 9/10 May 1996, a female at Loch Naver on 10 May 1988, an adult male flying north-east over Handa on 10 May 1993 and a male flying north at Loch Lucy on 24 May 1995.

Hen Harrier *Circus cyaneus* (Breeding resident and passage migrant.)
After its virtual extermination as a mainland Scottish breeding species at the end of the last century the Hen Harrier took advantage of a reduction in keepering during the Second World War to make a comeback. In Sutherland it still suffers persecution on some grouse moors but, in compensation, has benefited from the more secure nesting sites afforded by young forestry plantations.

The population is currently estimated to be about 30 pairs. In 1971, young fledged from a nest near Dornoch on the exceptionally early date of 12 June (MacDonald 1972). Wing-tagged females in the south-east have proved to be mainly of Easter Ross origin. The species is scarcest in the west. Single 'ringtails' were on Handa on 26 May 1985, 27 May 1993 and 16 June 1984.

Autumn birds include a few passage migrants from the Northern Isles and/or Scandinavia. There were five different 'ringtails' in the Brora area on 8 November 1990 and one flew south-west over the sea off Brora on 8 December 1990. Winter numbers fluctuate but are usually fairly low.

Montagu's Harrier *Circus pygargus* (Vagrant from Europe.)
A male on Handa on 23 May 1979 is the only record.

Goshawk *Accipiter gentilis* (Scarce breeding resident.)
The origins of the Scottish population, which began to re-establish itself in the 1950s, are uncertain. The majority may have been escapes. Despite persecution and egg-collecting the species seems to be on the increase. In Sutherland it has a fairly secure toe-hold. There are recent reports from central, western and northern sites, as well as several in the south.

Sparrowhawk *Accipiter nisus* (Common breeding resident and passage migrant.)
Although widely distributed, Sparrowhawks are at their greatest density in the more diverse habitats of the south-east, where they are the scourge of garden bird tables. The breeding population is probably increasing with the spread and growth of the new forests.

Autumn migrants, presumably from Scandinavia, occur in the north and east in September and October. An immigrant flying south-west over the Moray Firth off Brora on 5 September 1992 was attacked by a Great Skua. Three were seen in just five minutes at Trantlemore, Strath Halladale, on 30 September 1991.

Buzzard *Buteo buteo* (Common breeding resident.)
Visitors from southern Britain are often astounded by the numbers of Buzzards in Sutherland, particularly in the south-east where they thrive on the abundant rabbit population. It is quite normal to see 25-40 birds on a circuit of rather fewer miles. In early January 1997 there were at least 75 on the coastal strip between Dornoch and Helmsdale.

The population has increased considerably over the last 40 years, probably due to reduced persecution. Breeding densities, and breeding success, are lower in central areas and parts of the north and west. A nest at Forsinain in June 1994 contained the remains of a Short-eared Owl.

A partially albino bird near Kinbrace in early June 1993 was about 90% white and attracted more than its fair share of mobbing.

Some migrants may pass through in autumn. Several birds from a flock of 15 over Clynelish, Brora on 21 August 1994 (when a Rough-leg also arrived) left high to the south-west.

Rough-legged Buzzard *Buteo lagopus* (Very scarce passage migrant and rare winter visitor.)
The normal route across the North Sea for migrants reaching the east coast of Britain from Scandinavia lies well to the south of Sutherland, where the species is far from annual. There have been five spring records: singles flying east over Borgie Forest on 29 March 1986, at Strath Beg on 22 April 1990, Embo on 19 May 1976, Loch Merkland on 30 May 1984 and Creag Meadie on 6 June 1989.

More surprisingly, the species has been recorded twice in August: at Loch Buidhe on 14 August 1976 and at Clynelish, Brora on 21 August 1994. The latter, an adult, was almost certainly an early migrant as conditions were ideal for a North Sea crossing. Adult Rough-legs are known to move south-west from their Scandinavian breeding territories in August and the occasional 'overshoot' in optimum weather conditions might be expected. There was one at Durness on 18 September 1965 and one at Loch Loyal on 11 November 1969. Note the complete absence of October arrivals – often the peak month further south.

There are only three recent winter records: one at Forsinain on 9 December 1993 (reported several times from Strath Halladale that winter); one flew south-east through Strath Brora on 26 January 1997; one at Ben Bhraggie, Golspie, in February 1991.

Beware! Several 'Rough-legs' reported in recent years have proved to be pale morph Common Buzzard 'look-alikes', which are not uncommon in Sutherland.

Golden Eagle *Aquila chrysaetos* (Breeding resident.)

Although a few pairs hang on in the south-east, where it has been persecuted by some sheep farmers and gamekeepers, eagles are typically birds of the so-called 'deer forest' (largely tree-less expanses of open moorland) and the mountain ranges of west and central Sutherland. A national survey in 1992 showed a small overall decline in the Scottish population over a ten-year period, but a 27% decrease in eastern Sutherland – the largest decline in Scotland. The population in 1992 was around 60 pairs (Green 1996).

Immature birds wander widely outside the breeding season and it is in winter they are most likely to be seen near the east coast.

Osprey *Pandion haliaetus* (Breeding summer visitor and passage migrant.)
Following its extinction in the nineteenth century, well documented
re-colonisation of Speyside (probably from Scandinavia) and subsequent
expansion, Ospreys first bred in Sutherland again in the late 1970s. By
1996 there were several pairs. Birds are increasingly seen away from the
main breeding areas, suggesting the likelihood of a continuing growth in
the population. Sadly, egg collectors still remain the greatest obstacle to this.

Typically, the first arrivals reach the south-east in the first half of April
(31 March in 1993). Most have departed before mid September. An
exceptionally late bird was seen over Strathy Forest on 6 November 1994.
Singles flying south-west through the Clynelish valley, Brora (the main
east coast fly-way) on 5 August 1994 and 9 August 1995 were most probably of Scandinavian origin.

Kestrel *Falco tinnunculus* (Common breeding resident.)
Widely distributed, but least common in the areas of higher rainfall in the
west. Many of Sutherland's breeding birds are summer visitors although
coastal populations remain quite high in mild winters. A few migrants
might be expected to pass through in autumn but there is little evidence
for this.

Red-footed Falcon *Falco vespertinus* (Rare passage migrant.)
There are only three records: singles at Meikle Ferry on 1 May 1973,
Loch Loyal on 5 July 1967 and Durness on 22 July 1967.

Merlin *Falco columbarius* (Breeding summer visitor and passage migrant.
Scarce in winter.)
Merlins are unobtrusive in the breeding season and there may be rather
more breeding pairs than the few records suggest – perhaps about 50 in
total. The main arrival takes place in March/April. Some of these birds are
probably passing through on their way further north, as on 29 April 1993
when four different individuals flew north-east through the Clynelish
valley in less than two hours.

Autumn passage occurs from late August to October, when birds have
been seen well offshore from Brora. Occasional birds are seen in winter.

Hobby *Falco subbuteo* (Rare passage migrant.)
The two summer records were within a day of each other: one at
Dornoch on 24 June 1990 and one flying south-west along the east coast
fly-way through the Clynelish valley, Brora on 25 June 1992 (a year in
which unusual numbers of southern falcons reached the Northern Isles).
There are four autumn records between 12 and 29 September (1972-91)
and an immature was seen at Embo on 21 October 1984.

Gyrfalcon *Falco rusticolus* (Rare winter visitor and passage migrant.)
Two were shot in the first half of the twentieth century: at Rogart on
8 March 1910 and at Torrisdale (undated) in 1937.

On 29 August 1992 I was sea-watching in fine weather at Brora when a
large, heavily built, grey-brown falcon arrived from east of north-east,
sending the gulls and terns into a panic. It came very close in, then veered
away across the Firth towards Tarbatness. Although the BBRC, perhaps
suspicious of falconers' escapes and the early date, did not accept it, I am
sure it was a Gyr on size, build and diagnostic tail pattern. Brown (1976)
states that young Gyrs become independent of their parents from about
mid August so, as with Rough-legged Buzzard, the possibility of a wandering bird from the Scandinavian population 'overshooting' the North
Sea in fine weather in late August is not as unlikely as it first seems.

Peregrine *Falco peregrinus* (Breeding resident and partial migrant.)
Highland Peregrines did not suffer the full effects of the population crash
in the 1950s and 1960s caused by pesticide residues (Ratcliffe 1980) and
provided an important reservoir of birds for the natural re-colonisation of
sites in southern Britain. However, the Sutherland population has been
slow to recover to its pre-war level of around 58 pairs. Illegal egg collecting
and the taking of chicks by maverick falconers is probably to blame. In
1991 about 45 pairs were thought to have bred, of which only 13 were
coastal (D. A. Ratcliffe).

Adults are semi-resident; most of the young move away for the winter.

Red Grouse *Lagopus lagopus scoticus* (Breeding resident.)
Although numbers of grouse are known to fluctuate cyclically, there seems

to have been a marked decline in the south-east in recent years, possibly related to the increased incidence of a fatal tick-borne disease. In some areas over-enthusiastic or ill-controlled muirburning may also be a contributory factor. Breeding density was always lower in the west. Chicks from the very small Handa population are sometimes taken by skuas but two pairs successfully raised a total of 12 young in 1991 and three pairs fledged eight young in 1993.

Ptarmigan *Lagopus mutus* (Breeding resident.)
Like the Red Grouse, Ptarmigan numbers fluctuate naturally but they are never very high. It is found mainly on the higher tops in western and northern Sutherland but at increasingly low elevations (down to 300 m, 984 ft) towards Cape Wrath in the north west. One was seen at only 125 m (410 ft) near Bettyhill on 13 October 1983. This species is likely to be one of the first casualties of global warming.

Black Grouse *Tetrao tetrix* (Uncommon breeding resident.)
Although considered 'numerous' in the nineteenth century, this species is no longer common, although it is probably under-recorded. Good numbers breed in the plantations to the north of Lairg and doubtless elsewhere in forested central areas. There were five reports in 1991, including five males at a lek in the south-east in April (where only two were present in April 1994) and five females near Kintradwell, Brora on 20 October.

Capercaillie *Tetrao urogallus* (Formerly a scarce breeder, now possibly rare.)
The decline of this (re-introduced) species is associated with the loss and fragmentation of native pinewoods. Only one such area now survives in the extreme south of Sutherland. At present it is not large enough to support a viable population, but a large-scale regeneration project involving neighbouring Estates offers hope for the future. Until then, most sightings are likely to be of the folk group of this name. The last definite record was of one at Carbisdale on 2 November 1986 but there are recent unconfirmed reports from a wood in the south-east.

[Bobwhite] *Colinus virginianus* (Escape.)
Several birds were at large, by accident or design, in the Brora area in 1995 and may have attempted to breed. None was seen in 1996, following a hard winter.

[Red-legged Partridge] *Alectoris rufa* (Introduction.)
Several releases (probably mainly of Red-leg/Chukar hybrids) have been made since the first at Rosehall in 1970 but none has proved a success. The odd pair may still breed on Coul Links at Loch Fleet.

Grey Partridge *Perdix perdix* (Scarce breeding resident.)
Very thinly distributed along coastal farmland and links in the south-east and north. Two or three pairs breed annually on Coul Links, Loch Fleet and there is a small population between Kintradwell and Portgower. Four were seen at Balcharn, Lairg, in October 1996. In the north, one or two pairs breed in the Melvich area and there were seven at Balnakeil on 26 October 1985. Coveys of up to a dozen birds are seen in autumn.

Quail *Coturnix coturnix* (Irregular and rare summer visitor; occasionally breeds.)
As populations of this migratory gamebird continue to suffer from hunting pressures in the Mediterranean and elsewhere, fewer are likely to reach Sutherland. Quails have been reported in only four recent years: one calling male near Loch Fleet in July/August 1985, one at Ledmore on 28 June 1988, two or three at Loch Fleet, two at Cape Wrath on 5 July and five elsewhere in summer 1989 (a major Quail year) and, in the extreme north, a pair with four young at Ribigill on 11 August 1992.

Harvie-Brown and Buckley (1887) refer to two being obtained at Helmsdale in November 1879.

Pheasant *Phasianus colchicus* (Breeding resident (originally introduced).)
I have to admit to some disappointment at finding, on moving north to Sutherland, that Pheasants had preceded me by almost 150 years and were well established even on the north coast of the Scottish mainland (though still scarce in the west). The population is augmented by frequent releases.

Water Rail *Rallus aquaticus* (Scarce passage migrant and winter visitor; may have bred.)
The species has been heard in the breeding season in the west, but not for many years.

It used to be seen occasionally in winter in the Dornoch area, but there have been no recent sightings there. One was heard at Rhilochan on 24 March 1991and one found dead at Rogart on 13 December 1987. As a passage migrant, it is most likely to occur on the north coast. The last there was one at Durness on 30 October 1982.

Spotted Crake *Porzana porzana* (Rare summer visitor and passage migrant. Has probably bred.)
In the west, birds were heard calling at a marsh in each spring and summer between 1966 and 1970. One was calling at a site in the south-east from 8-27 May 1994. The only autumn record is of a bird found freshly killed at Balnakeil on 14 October 1984.

Baillon's Crake *Porzana pusilla* (Vagrant from southern Europe.)
One was shot at Loch Cracail, north-east of Inveran, in 1844.

Corncrake *Crex crex* (Breeding summer visitor in very small numbers; rare passage migrant.)
The decline of this species in mainland Britain as a result of changes in agricultural practice is well documented. The reduction in traditional crofting has contributed to its plight in Sutherland. Harvie-Brown and Buckley (1887) descibed it as 'very abundant' in the east in the nineteenth century but rare in the west. About 40 pairs were thought to have bred in the late 1970s (Angus 1983). Since 1982, a few calling males have been reported annually from the extreme north and north-west, with the occasional bird in the south-east. The exception was 1991, when at least ten birds were heard in the north. One calling on Handa on 11 June 1993 was the first there since 1989.

It is hardly surprising such a secretive bird is rarely seen on migration. One was found injured in Golspie on 10 September 1990 and there was one on Faraid Head on 16 October 1994.

Moorhen *Gallinula chloropus* (Scarce breeding resident and passage migrant.)
This is another species which has declined in recent years but the reasons
are less clear cut than those which accounted for the Corncrake. It was
never common and may be undergoing natural range contraction. Several
pairs used to nest in the Dornoch area but by 1995 there was only one
pair at Cuthill, although birds may continue to breed at Loch Evelix and
Loch Ospisdale. It has shown itself to be an opportunistic breeder at Loch
Fleet, where four pairs bred on flooded dune slacks in 1988, but only one
pair in 1990 (Vaughan 1991). There were birds at several sites in central
and western areas in the mid 1970s. Single pairs nested by Loch Eriboll in
1989 and at Duart Mor in 1996 .

One or two presumed migrants are regularly seen at Melvich in
September/October. Despite a series of milder winters (before 95/96!)
there were few reports of overwintering birds. One remained on the river
near Brora from 15 January-14 April 1992. It is probable that most of
'our' birds are in fact summer visitors – one at Rhilochan, Knockarthur,
on 24 March 1991 being newly returned.

Coot *Fulica atra* (Scarce breeder and winter visitor.)
Although it has bred occasionally in the past in both the south-east and
the north-west (and may still do so at Loch Evelix and Loch Ospisdale),
Coots are now a rare sight in Sutherland. Single birds appeared on Loch
Croispol, Durness, in three successive winters in the mid 1980s. There
were two at Culrain on 5 January 1994, one on Loch Caladail on
6 December 1993 and two at Duart Mor on 27 December 1984.

Crane *Grus grus* (Rare passage migrant.)
One flew purposefully south-west over Brora on the evening of 29 April
1996 (probably the bird which left North Ronaldsay on 27 April). One
was seen at Loth and Brora on 14 May 1983.

In the past, there was one at Oldshoremore from 20-28 June 1969 and
one at Loth on 6 August 1958.

Oystercatcher *Haematopus ostralegus* (Common breeding resident, passage
migrant and winter visitor.)

Widespread breeder around the coasts, spreading inland during the twentieth century. Sites are re-occupied from late February near the coast and in March further inland. A breeding density of over 12 pairs per sq km (0.6 sq mile) has been calculated in suitable areas of the south-east (Angus 1983). Up to 50 pairs nest in the Loch Fleet area. The Handa population seems stable at around 25-30 pairs.

Most of the inland breeders and some of the young from coastal nests travel south in the winter (Swann 1985), when numbers are augmented by arrivals from Scandinavia, Iceland and the Northern Isles. Birds ringed at Brora and Dornoch have been recovered in Ireland and France and a French-ringed bird was found at Brora.

The largest concentrations occur in the Dornoch Firth and at Loch Fleet, which between them account for the majority of the 5000+ birds wintering in Sutherland. The high proportion of adults suggests the majority of young birds leave Sutherland for the winter.

Black-winged Stilt *Himantopus himantopus* (Vagrant from southern Europe.)
One was reported from Loch Brora on 20 April 1953 but the record (erroneously given as Moray) was no longer considered acceptable for inclusion in *Birds in Scotland* (Thom 1986). Harvie-Brown and Buckley (1887) also refer to a bird shot at Brora in July 1855 but they were unable to trace the specimen after the sale of the owner's collection. It seems unlikely such an unmistakable species could have been misidentified.

Avocet *Recurvirostra avosetta* (Rare passage migrant.)
Four at Loch Fleet on 25 August 1982 and one at Dornoch Spit from 31 March-2 April 1984 are the only records.

Ringed Plover *Charadrius hiaticula* (Common breeding resident and passage migrant.)
Nests widely around the coasts and also inland by lochs, to which it moves from about late March. The largest breeding densities are in the south-east with normally up to 25 pairs at Loch Fleet (32 pairs in 1990).

Spring migrants probably include birds en route to Greenland and even

Newfoundland. Autumn birds certainly include some small, dark individuals of the race *tundrae*. One ringed at Dornoch in September 1982 was recovered in Morocco in December 1986.

Flocks of up to 150 can be seen at Brora and Loch Fleet in autumn and winter. The highest recent count was 213 at Brora on 16 December 1990.

Kentish Plover *Charadrius alexandrinus* (Vagrant from southern Europe.)
A male was found at Brora on 27 May 94 – a classic 'overshooting' day with high pressure extending well to the south. In the evening it began calling excitedly and left high to the north-east with a small party of Dunlin.

Dotterel *Charadrius morinellus* (Scarce breeding summer visitor and passage migrant.)
Recent survey work by SNH has shown Dotterels to be present in flocks on several, mainly western, tops in late April/early May. Most of these birds quickly move on, presumably to Scandinavia, but a few pairs stay to breed. The population is probably in excess of 20 pairs in good years. Breeding has occurred as low as 320 m (1050 ft) in the extreme north.

Single migrants occurred at Loch Fleet in early May 1989 and 1994. One was seen high on Quinaig as late as 25 September 1994.

Golden Plover *Pluvialis apricaria* (Fairly common breeding resident and passage migrant.)
Surveys in the 1970s and 1980s showed this species to be the most abundant wader on the peatlands of Sutherland and Caithness. More recent work suggests that, in addition to direct losses to forestry, about 220 pairs have been lost on open ground in recent years, leaving a breeding population of around 3760 pairs in the two counties (Whitfield 1996).

Breeding densities vary but are lower in the north-west (about one pair per sq km/0.6 sq mile) than the south-east (two-three pairs). Birds wintering on or near coasts move back onto inland hills if the weather is mild enough. Late snow forces them down to straths and beaches, e.g. 150 at Brora on 23 March 1993.

Sixty-six on Handa on 24 May 1985 were presumably late migrants. Autumn passage is evident on coasts from late July/August. Several flocks arrived from the north west at Strathy Point on 28 September 1996.

A colour-ringed bird at Brora on 25 January 1993 had been marked on North Ronaldsay and seen on South Humberside on 2 September 1992.

Grey Plover *Pluvialis squatarola* (Uncommon passage migrant and winter visitor.)
The only locality which reliably attracts flocks of Grey Plovers is the Dornoch Spit. Numbers peak there in October (maximum over 50 on 3 October 1993). The highest recent winter count is 26 on 20 January 1985.

Elsewhere the species is scarce. Small numbers occur intermittently at Brora and Loch Fleet, where it has been seen in every month except July, but mostly in late spring and autumn. There were three on Handa on 26 April 1982 and singles there on 17 May and 6 June 1985. Autumn migrants, which first appear in mid-August, include ones and twos in the north in late September/early October. A bird ringed at Loch Fleet on 2 October 1983 was recovered in France five years later.

Lapwing *Vanellus vanellus* (Mainly breeding summer visitor but some winter on coasts.)
Lapwings have declined in the last 20 years. They re-occupy inland breeding territories in the lower Straths in February and higher ground in March, when pre-breeding flocks assemble on coastal fields. Typically birds of grassland, surveys of breeding waders on the peatlands showed them to be present on less than a third of the sites visited and then mainly ones with marginal agricultural improvement (Stroud et al 1987). Breeding density in optimum habitat in the south-east was estimated at 42 pairs per sq km (0.6 sq mile) (Angus 1983) in the 1970s. The species breeds at much lower densities in the north and west. Most birds leave the breeding areas in July, when flocks build up on coasts.

There is little evidence of coastal movement in either spring or autumn although eight came in from the sea at Strathy Point on 3 March 1986. A nestling ringed near Dornoch in June 1982 was recovered in Ireland the following January – the likely destination of many Sutherland birds.

At Loch Fleet, there were peak counts of over 600 in 1979 and 1981. Since the mid 1980s flocks of more than 100 are unusual.

Knot *Calidris canutus* (Passage migrant and winter visitor in variable numbers.)

The migratory movements of Knot are complex, which partly explains their rather unpredictable appearances in Sutherland. Whilst most Scottish birds originate from breeding populations to the north-west (Greenland and Canada) they reach us via moulting grounds in the Wadden Sea and the Wash, where an autumn bird recovered in Sutherland had been ringed.

The spring passage is normally slight: 35 at Brora on 8 May 1995 is the highest recent total at that locality. A few adults re-appear from July (earliest 10th at Handa). Juveniles follow from late August. Numbers build up in September/October, e.g. 509 at Brora on 14 October 1983. Only small parties are seen in the north and west.

Winter peaks have declined from the 3000 counted on the Dornoch Firth in the 1970s. The largest recent counts are of 2000 at Embo on 11 December 1988 and 1300 at Dornoch on 12 January 1997.

Sanderling *Calidris alba* (Winter visitor and passage migrant in small numbers but recorded in every month.)

The wintering population is fairly stable at 20-30 birds, mainly at Brora. These birds have usually departed by mid April. Spring passage is mainly in May/June. There were 29 at Brora on 7 May 1993, 26 at Balnakeil on 2 June 1988 and a late flock of 29 at Loch Fleet on 14 June 1989. A colour-ringed bird at Handa on 24 May 1985 had spent the previous winter at Teesmouth and had been seen there only three days before.

Summering birds are occasionally seen on beaches in the north and west and there is an intriguing record of a pair displaying on a northern mountain on 15 June 1973.

The first autumn migrants normally appear in mid or late July. There were 26 at Balnakeil on 22 August 1991 and 30 at Dornoch on 26 August 1984.

Little Stint *Calidris minutus* (Passage migrant, usually scarce.)

The only spring record is of two at Colaboll on 15 April 1984.

In autumn, extreme dates are 10 July and 16 October. Only in exceptional years, when easterlies in late August/September bring numbers of juveniles to the east coast, can more than a few be seen. In 1965, numbers at Dornoch peaked at 230 on 21 August. A flock of 25 was seen there on 22 September 1995.

Temminck's Stint *Calidris temminckii* (Rare summer visitor (may breed) and passage migrant.)
This sub-Arctic breeder first attempted to nest in the Cairngorms in the 1930s. Since the 1960s small numbers have nested regularly in northern Scotland but there are few records for Sutherland. One gave the distraction display in suitable breeding habitat on 29 May 1962. There was a migrant on Handa on 2 June 1976, two near Lairg on 9 July 1985 and one east of Melvich on 10 July 1976.

White-rumped Sandpiper *Calidris fuscicollis* (Vagrant from North America.)
One at Dornoch on 23 October 1977 is the only record.

Pectoral Sandpiper *Calidris melanotos* (Vagrant from North America.)
One on Handa from 25-28 July 1975, is somewhat surprisingly, the only record of this common American species which reaches Britain annually in small numbers. A bird displaying in the 'flow' country in the spring of 1974 was just on the wrong side of the Caithness boundary, but was apparently visible from Sutherland!

Curlew Sandpiper *Calidris ferruginea* (Scarce autumn passage migrant.)
Although this species is fairly common on autumn passage further south in Britain, in Sutherland it has been seen in only six of the last 15 years: two at Littleferry in August 1988, up to six at Dornoch in September 1984, two at Brora on 13 September 1995 and juveniles at Brora on 15 September 1985, 10 October 1991 and 18 October 1993.

Purple Sandpiper *Calidris maritima* (Winter visitor and passage migrant. A potential breeder.)
A small breeding population of Purple Sandpipers has recently become established in the Highlands but none has yet been found in Sutherland.

The Moray Firth represents the dividing line between wintering birds of Norwegian origin in north-eastern Scotland and longer-billed birds of mainly Icelandic origin in Sutherland. The former begin arriving in July and a few of these reach Sutherland's coasts but do not stay long. Two adults appeared at Brora on 12 July 1992, one flew north there on 12 July 1995 and another was seen on 22 July 1994. Birds in July and August on Handa are more likely to be summering non-breeders from the north-western population. One which flew west past Strathy Point on 27 September 1994 may have been an early arrival from Iceland. Birds from this population do not normally reach us until late October.

The number of wintering birds in the south-east has declined in recent years. A maximum of 48 at Brora in the early 1990s compares with counts of over 100 in the early 1980s. In winters 1995/96 and 96/97 the total there was below 20. Flocks also occur at Embo and Helmsdale. Forty-five at Melvich on 24 February 1979 is the highest number reported from the north.

Up to 65 occur on Handa (from which winter data are lacking) in April and early May. In the south-east, a few birds hang on until mid May.

Dunlin *Calidris alpina* (Breeding summer visitor to uplands; common passage migrant and winter resident on coasts.)
After Golden Plover, Dunlin was the commonest breeding wader found during surveys of the peatlands of Sutherland and Caithness in the 1980s, being present on 71 of the 77 sites visited. A 1995 survey shows that some 735 pairs have been lost on open ground since 1987 to add to the losses to forestry, leaving a breeding population of just over 3000 pairs in the two counties (Whitfield 1996). Densities vary enormously as the birds are semi-colonial, concentrating in areas with the greatest abundance of dubh lochans. The median density was calculated at 1.76 pairs per sq km (0.6 sq mile) (Stroud et al 1987). Birds return to breeding territories from mid to late April.

Visible passage in spring is slight with small numbers on Handa from April to June and a few on north and east coasts. A few non-breeders in summer. Numbers increase again in July and August as local birds are joined by migrants from the north-east , Iceland and Greenland. By mid

August there are normally about 100 at Loch Fleet. Small southward movements off the east coast and westward movements off the north coast are evident from late August to early October.

Trapping has produced controls of birds ringed in Denmark, Norway, Sweden, Finland, Poland and Germany and recoveries from the Netherlands, Denmark, Norway, Finland, Poland and Germany.

Winter populations in the south-east vary considerably, from less than 1000 to notable peaks of at least 6000 at Dornoch on 5 January 1989 and 5000 there on 12 January 1997. Normally only a few hundred winter at Loch Fleet, but there were 2000 there on 23 December 1984.

Stilt Sandpiper *Micropalama himantopus* (Vagrant from North America.)
The sole record – one at Dornoch on 18 April 1970 – was particularly notable as the first spring sighting in Britain as well as being a new bird for Scotland.

Buff-breasted Sandpiper *Tryngites subruficollis* (Vagrant from North America.)
One at Dornoch on 25 September 1960 is the only record. After Pectoral Sandpiper, this confiding species is perhaps the most likely American wader to occur in Sutherland, which has an abundance of its preferred autumn habitat – short coastal grassland.

Ruff *Philomachus pugnax (*Scarce passage migrant; has bred.)
In 1980 a nest with four eggs was found near Altnaharra, the clutch hatching successfully. Although the species re-colonised eastern England in the nineteen sixties from the Low Countries, birds from the north Scandinavian breeding population were most likely involved.

As a passage migrant, the species is rare in spring: two at Loch Fleet on 30 April 1993 and a female at Mudale on 26 May 1991 are the only recent records. Small numbers are seen in most autumns, mainly in the south-east, from late July to September, maximum nine on 30 July. A total of five birds was reported in August 1989. The latest were two at Dornoch on 25 September 1984.

Jack Snipe *Lymnocryptes minimus* (Winter visitor in small numbers; probably overlooked.)

The paucity of records over the last 15 years may represent a genuine decline, although there are widely scattered sightings in the 1990s from Handa (April) in the west, to the north coast and to Dornoch in the south-east. Birds flushed at three central peatland sites during survey work between 14 and 26 April 1995 suggest a more marked spring passage than is otherwise evident.

Extreme dates for the species are 15 October and 29 April. A bird ringed at Dornoch on 29 November 1980 was recovered in Sligo, Ireland the following January.

In winter, birds are sometimes driven to beaches in hard weather, exceptionally six at Dornoch on 23 December 1979. This suggests either late immigration or a larger wintering population in the hinterland than the lack of records at this season would indicate.

Snipe *Gallinago gallinago* (Breeding resident, passage migrant and winter visitor.)

The breeding population is widely distributed from coastal fringes and inland straths to upland peatlands. In mild winters birds begin moving inland from late February and display flights commence about mid March. Breeding densities are difficult to calculate but probably range from about five pairs per sq km (0.6 sq mile) in optimum lowland habitat to less than one pair per sq km (0.6 sq mile) on the higher moorlands. On Handa, 29 pairs bred in 1985 and 31 pairs in 1993.

In autumn, migrants have been seen coming in from the east from late August to mid November. Some of these birds show the characteristics of the race *faroensis*.

Most of our breeders probably move south for the winter and the relatively few seen at that season are probably immigrants from Iceland, the Northern Isles or Scandinavia.

Woodcock *Scolopax rusticola* (Breeding resident, passage migrant and winter visitor.)

The species apparently colonised the south-east in the mid nineteenth century. It is now widely distributed and 'roding' can now be heard over all types of woodland in spring and summer. Some have also nested on open moorland. Singles occurred on Handa on 11 April 1985 (only the second record for the island) and 28 May 1993.

Some local breeders probably move south for the winter but their numbers are more than replenished by immigrants from Scandinavia. These begin arriving in October (earliest two at Strathy Point on 17 October 1986). 'Good numbers' were reported from the Bonar Bridge area in November/December 1984. The species becomes most obvious in winter hard snaps when they are forced to feed during the day, often in uncharacteristically open situations.

Black-tailed Godwit *Limosa limosa* (Scarce passage migrant and occasional winter visitor.)
Small numbers are seen in most years on their way to and from their Icelandic breeding grounds. Spring passage normally begins in mid April, although one at Loch Fleet on 3 March 1996 and three at the Kyle of Tongue on 19 March 1993 may have been early migrants. Most records are of singles but there were up to four at Colaboll on 15/16 April 1984 and 25 at Loch Fleet on 1 May 1986. There was one at The Mound on 17 June 1992.
The return movement begins in late July. Again, single birds are the norm but there were six on Handa on 30 August 1984. An adult at Loch Fleet on 6 October 1979 is the latest.

The only recent winter sighting is of a flock of 20 at the Kyle of Tongue on 19 January 1991.

Bar-tailed Godwit *Limosa lapponica* (Common winter visitor and passage migrant.)
Wintering numbers are variable and probably reflect conditions in Europe. Exceptionally low temperatures on the Continent no doubt accounted for the record count of 1800 at Dornoch on 12 January 1997. Up to 1500 were counted at Dornoch and 500 at Loch Fleet in the early 1980s. Few are seen in the north and west, maximum 30 at the Kyle of Tongue on 13 January 1991. Colour marking has shown that some birds

do not reach the Dornoch Firth until mid winter and, like the Knot, come via the Wash.

Most of the wintering birds have departed by early May, although a few non-breeders summer. The first returning adults appear in mid July with the bulk arriving in August/September. Again, relatively few are seen away from the south-east.

Whimbrel *Numenius phaeopus* (Passage migrant and occasional breeder.) Britain's breeding Whimbrel are almost exclusively confined to the Northern Isles but there are intermittent reports from the Scottish mainland. Most of Sutherland's breeding records, since the first in 1961, are from the north and west but a pair nested successfully near the east coast in 1995 and again in 1996.

The first spring migrants normally arrive around 20 April (earliest 12th). Parties of up to 15 pass through in May.

The return passage starts in mid July (earliest 9th). Twenty-two flew south over the Moray Firth off Brora on 16 July 1993 and a total of 28 came in from Hoy at Strathy Point on 1 August 1996, all turning to the west. Six flew south off Brora on 13 August 1992 but most August/September records are of ones and twos and probably include both Icelandic and Scandinavian birds. None has been seen later than mid-September, with the exception of a November straggler at Dornoch.

Curlew *Numenius arquata* (Breeding resident, passage migrant and winter visitor.)
Common and widespread, though in smaller numbers in the north and west. Breeding densities vary from up to seven pairs per sq km (0.6 sq mile) in damp rough pasture in parts of the south-east to less than 0.5 pairs per sq km (0.6 sq mile) in the 'unimproved' peatlands. Inland territories are occupied from as early as late February.

Inland breeders move to the coast in late June/ July and up to 500 can be seen at Loch Fleet and 400 at Dornoch in late July/August. Many of our birds are thought to move south for the winter, being replaced in autumn and winter by birds of mainly Scandinavian origin. Small arrivals from the north-east have been noted at Brora from 25 June.

Mid winter numbers in the south-east are slightly lower than the autumn peak, maxima 355 at Loch Fleet on 19 January 1992 and 380 at Dornoch on 6 February 1988.

Spotted Redshank *Tringa erythropus* (Scarce passage migrant, mainly in autumn.)
Two at Dornoch on 24 April 1966 is the only spring record. One arrived from the east at Brora on 25 June 1992.

In autumn the species has been reported in only six of the last 15 years between 3 August and 14 October, mainly in late August. All records are of single birds except for two adults at Brora on 26 August 1991.

Redshank *Tringa totanus* (Breeding resident, passage migrant, winter visitor.)
Widely distributed but scarcer in the north and west. Unlike in many parts of Scotland, there is no indication of any marked decline in the population. Breeding densities are at their highest on marginal farmland in the south-east where up to five pairs per sq km (0.6 sq mile) have been found. Only scattered pairs nest on the north-western peatlands. Local concentrations can occur where conditions permit – for example, four pairs nested in a two acre (0.8 ha) field near Melvich in 1984. Inland ter-ritories are occupied in March, birds moving back to the coast as soon as the young have fledged.

Spring coastal flocks, such as 170 at Dornoch on 3 April 1988 and 265 at Loch Fleet in April 1989, probably consist mainly of Icelandic breeders. These birds are gone by mid-May and begin returning in late July.

East coast numbers build up rapidly in August. In the west, a maxi-mum count of 65 on Handa was in early September. Most of the Sutherland breeders are thought to move south for the winter and Icelandic immigrants are mainly responsible for the autumn peak (early to mid October). A bird ringed at Heimaey, Iceland in June 1977 was controlled at Brora on 4 October 1980. The largest counts are of 450 at Loch Fleet on 6 October 1991 and 292 at Dornoch on 11 October 1992.

Up to 400 normally winter at Loch Fleet and the Dornoch Firth, with smaller numbers elsewhere. Colour ringing has shown that new birds arrive in the Moray Firth in mid winter from estuaries further south.

Greenshank *Tringa nebularia* (Breeding summer visitor and passage migrant; rare in winter.)

Sutherland is the Greenshank's British stronghold with about 350 pairs (roughly 40% of the national breeding population). It is widely distributed but densities are highest in the north-west, where they have been calculated to be two pairs per sq km (0.6 sq mile) (Nethersole-Thompson and Nethersole-Thompson 1979). About 130 pairs were lost to new afforestation between 1979 and 1985 and, more worryingly, a further 165 pairs have been lost on open ground since (Whitfield 1996).

The first birds normally arrive at the end of March (earliest 25th). Dispersal from the breeding sites to lochs and coasts occurs from late June. Up to 25 congregate at Loch Fleet in July. The species is relatively scarce after the end of July, although migrants are seen at Loch Fleet, where there were still nine on 19 August 1985, until October.

There are no recent winter records but one or two were seen in several winters at Skibo or Loch Fleet between 1959 and 1977 and the odd bird has also been seen in the north.

Lesser Yellowlegs *Tringa flavipes* (Vagrant from North America.)
One at Dornoch from 31 August to 7 September 1980 is the only record.

Green Sandpiper *Tringa ochropus* (Scarce passage migrant; potential breeder.)
This species has bred once in Scotland and two beside an inland loch in Sutherland on 25 June 1968 indicate possible breeding. However, the date does not rule out returning migrants.

One at Dornoch on 1 May 1984 is the only recent spring record although it has occurred in the west at this season on several occasions in the past. Autumn migrants have been reported in only six of the last 15 years, from late July to September but mostly from 24 July to 7 August.

Wood Sandpiper *Tringa glareola* (Rare, occasionally breeding, summer visitor and scarce passage migrant.)
A pair nested in 1959 – the first time breeding was proved in Britain. Since then breeding has occurred in a number of years and may be more or less annual, but the numbers involved are very small.

Despite these regular summer arrivals, the species is hardly ever seen on passage. There was one at Loch Loyal on 23 April 1984, one at Balnakeil on 31 May 1991 and one at Dornoch on 13 August 1974.

Common Sandpiper *Actitis hypoleucos* (Common breeding summer visitor.)
Widely distributed, the high-pitched 'teetering' song is one of the most familiar summer sounds by lochs and rivers.

The first birds normally arrive towards the end of the third week of April but there was one at The Mound on 7 April 1996 and one at Bonar Bridge on 8 April 1983. Small concentrations occur in favoured coastal areas in late April/early May, e.g. 12 at the Mound on 1 May 1996, although most occupy their breeding territories immediately. Post breeding numbers sometimes reach 40 at The Mound/Loch Fleet in July. Scarce after mid August, there seems to be little in the way of autumn passage through Sutherland. Latest date 13 September 1992.

Turnstone *Arenaria interpres* (Winter visitor and passage migrant. May have bred.)
An agitated adult near an (unidentified) chick in the west in August 1976 is indicative of breeding but apparently not quite the proof such a

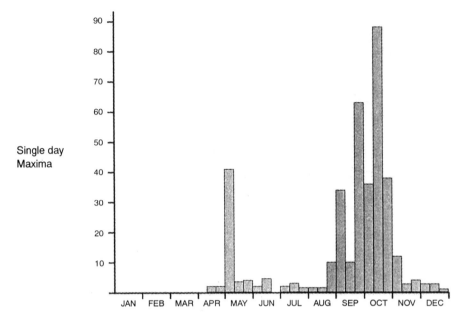

Pomarine Skuas in Sutherland

notable event requires. A few non-breeders sometimes summer on coasts.

Immigrants begin arriving in late July (earliest 18th in the south-east). Scottish birds are thought to originate mainly from the Greenland and north-east Canada breeding populations. Small parties were arriving from the north west at Strathy Point on 28 September 1996. Numbers peak in October, when up to 97 were counted at Brora and 50 at Littleferry in the early 1980s. More recently, the autumn peak at Brora has not exceeded 50 where winter numbers, too, are down in recent years. Relatively few winter on the west coast. Spring flocks include 80 at Embo on 18 April 1996 and 50 there on 17 May 1985.

Red-necked Phalarope *Phalaropus lobatus* (Formerly a scarce breeding summer visitor; now a rare migrant.)
The decline of this delightful species as a British breeding bird is well documented (e.g. Everett 1971). Occasional birds have been seen in summer in the flow country but it is many years since breeding was proved. The only recent record of a migrant is of one at Loch Fleet on 5 July 1994.

Grey Phalarope *Phalaropus fulicarius* (Scarce passage migrant.)
Up to 1982 the only record was of one at Handa on 3 September 1973.
Increased sea-watching in recent years has shown the species to be more
regular. One flew north at Brora on 5 March 1992, one flew west at
Strathy Point on 5 October 1996, two flew north-east off Lothbeg Point
on 13 October 1996, one came from the north-east into Kintradwell Bay
on 14 November 1993, one flew west at Strathy Point on 22 November
1995 and there was one at Dornoch on 3 December 1994.

Pomarine Skua *Stercorarius pomarinus* (Autumn passage migrant in the
north and east in variable numbers; mainly spring passage migrant in the
west.)
There is a regular northward passage off north-west Scotland in spring.
Most of these pass beyond the Outer Hebrides but birds have been seen
off the west coast between 25 April and 11 June, including 74 off Handa
between 1-5 May 1979. On the east coast, up to four have passed Brora
between 17 April and 12 May and an adult flew south there on 7 June 1995.

The first adults reappear in July (earliest 11th). Parties of migrants are
seen from late August.

A few 'Poms' usually linger in the Moray Firth in autumn, harassing

Kittiwakes. The occasional larger flights of these magnificent birds in autumn gales is one of the great spectacles of the sea-watching calendar. The largest movements in recent years have occurred between 7 September and 19 October, maxima 63 (52 adults) flying west at Strathy Point on 27 September 1994, 73 (mainly adults) flying north-east at Brora on 11 October 1992 and 88 flying north-east off Lothbeg Point on 13 October 1996. Smaller numbers are seen into November and ones or twos in December (latest 31st).

Arctic Skua *Stercorarius parasiticus* (Breeding summer visitor and passage migrant.)
A recent colonist, the species first bred on Handa in 1968. The colony there had increased to 35 pairs by 1985. Since then, numbers have fluctuated: 34 pairs bred in 1993, 27 in 1995 and 29 in 1996. A few pairs also breed in the flow country.

Breeding birds begin arriving in mid April (earliest 13th). There is also a northward passage of migrants off the west coast. Numbers are usually small but, in 1979, 148 were counted between 20 April and 6 May, including a loose flock of 65 on 3 May (Thorpe 1981). The species is very scarce off the east coast in spring but there are three recent records of up to three off Brora between 14-24 April.

Summer sightings are made off all coasts. Numbers build up in August as the young disperse and migrants arrive from further north. Unlike in southern Britain, however, Arctic is sometimes the least numerous skua on autumn sea-watches. Peak numbers occur in early September, maximum 46 flying north of Brora on 6 September 1992. Few are seen after September (latest 16 November).

Long-tailed Skua *Stercorarius longicaudus* (Passage migrant.)
Until fairly recently this elegant species was regarded as a British rarity. One flew north-west at Camore, Dornoch Firth, on 18 May 1956. There are four records of single birds at Handa between 21 May and 14 June, one at Scourie on 28 May 1984 and, in the north, one at Balnakeil on 24 June 1973.

A juvenile flying south at Brora on 6 September 1992 was the first county record for eight years and gave no hint of the events to come in 1994 and 1995. On 9 August 1994, a windless day with low cloud cover, a flock of 16 adults arrived at Brora from the south in mid morning and settled on the sea. A steady procession followed, including a flock of 26 in the afternoon, all heading north-east. In the evening a streak of bright sky on the south-western horizon encouraged ten to head south-west towards the Dornoch Firth, perhaps anticipating an overland crossing. The day's total was at least 69 – all adults.

At least 47 more (of which 45 were adults) passed Brora between 10 August and 19 October 1994. Fourteen adults flew west past Strathy Point on 27 September, proving this was not solely an east coast phenomenon.

1995 provided slightly less spectacular fare: 39 adults flew south-west at Brora on 7 August, followed by small numbers between 8 and 23 August; two adults flew west at Strathy Point on 27 August; singles flew north-east at Brora on 2 and 15 September, with three on 30 September.

1996 produced the earliest autumn record – two flying north-east off Brora on 29 July. The later passage was disappointing with the only multiples being parties of nine and three off Embo in mid August. Single adults were seen off Brora on 8 and 23 September and Strathy Point on 5 October.

Great Skua *Stercorarius skua* (Breeding summer visitor and passage migrant.)

The protection of some of Shetland's breeding colonies last century quickly led to a population increase, but it is only in the second half of this century that birds have bred in Sutherland. Handa, where the species bred for the first time in 1964, is the main site. In 1982 38 pairs bred and the total had risen to 80 pairs by 1990 (rearing an average of 1.2 young per pair) and 116 pairs by 1996. At least four pairs bred on Eilean nan Ron in 1981 and nine pairs in 1992. Since 1975, there have been a number of breeding records from the mainland in the west and north.

The first spring arrivals normally appear in early April (earliest 28 March). Numbers on spring passage are rather small. Both then and in summer, most are seen from the north and west coasts.

Larger movements off the north coast begin as early as mid July, typically

27 flying west off Strathy Point on 24 July 1996. Numbers increase on all coasts through August, when onshore winds concentrate passage at strategic headlands. Up to 30 have passed Brora but 91 flew west at Strathy Point on 27 August 1995. September maxima are 46 (mostly flying south) off Brora on 6 September in 1992 and 64 flying west off Strathy Point on 11 September in 1996. Fifty-two flew north-east off Lothbeg Point on 13 October 1996. Up to five per day have been seen in the first half of November and singles have occurred from late November to early January, with two off Brora on 1 January 1996.

Mediterranean Gull *Larus melanocephalus* (Vagrant from Europe.)
One in adult winter plumage at Brora on 12 October 1982 is the only record. The numbers of this species ocurring further south in Britain (where it is now breeding) have increased dramatically in the last 30 years and it may be expected to reach Sutherland more frequently in the future.

Laughing Gull *Larus atricilla* (Vagrant from North America.)
An immature moulting from first summer into second year plumage was enjoying easy pickings at the Dornoch beach caravan site when it was found on 13 August 1996. Its behaviour suggested it had been there for some time. It remained until at least 12 October.

Little Gull *Larus minutus* (Passage migrant in small numbers, mainly in the south-east. Occasional in winter.)
The numbers of Little Gulls occurring in Scotland has increased dramatically in the second half of this century. It is therefore surprising the species was still considered to be a very scarce migrant in Sutherland as recently as the 1980s. Intensive watching at the mouth of the River Brora, apparently the most favoured locality, has shown it to be of regular occurrence. During the last six years it has been seen there in every month except December, peaking in the first half of April and in late September/early October.

The majority of the birds are immatures or juveniles. Single adults have occurred in January (including one at Lothbeg Point on 6 January 1996), April (two on 12 April 1996), July (staying from 22 July-20 August

Little Gulls at Brora, 1990-1996

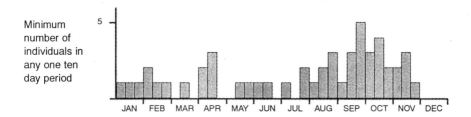

Minimum number of individuals in any one ten day period

1994), September (two on 13 September 1993), October and November. The largest total of birds (of any age) on a single day is five on 30 September 1994.

Sabine's Gull *Larus sabini* (Very scarce passage migrant.)
There have been six recent sightings of this rare Arctic breeder: one in first year plumage flying south-west off Brora on 26 April 1992 (an unusual date for a bird of this age in British waters), one off Golspie on 20 June 1985, an adult off Strathy Point in summer 1980, an adult off Dornoch on 20 September 1992 and juveniles flying west off Strathy Point on 28 September 1995 and 5 October 1996.

Bonaparte's Gull *Larus philadelphia* (Vagrant from North America.)
A sub-adult was seen at Scourie on 7 June 1973. Coincidentally, a sub-adult arrived from the south, with a Black-headed Gull, at Brora on 8 June 1992, bathed briefly in the river mouth, and left to the north-east. Although the diagnostic features were seen at close range, the record was not accepted by the BBRC.

Black-headed Gull *Larus ridibundus (*Common breeding resident, passage migrant and winter visitor.)
Breeding colonies are scattered through the east and north of the county, mainly on inland lochs with fringing vegetation and/or islands. There are few colonies in the west. The size of individual colonies increased greatly in the first half of the twentieth century (Pennie 1962) but one colony in

the south-east declined from about 100 pairs in 1991 to only 20 in 1996. Birds disperse to coasts, or further south, at the end of the breeding season. Resident birds are joined in autumn and winter by immigrants from (mainly) Iceland, Scandinavia and the Baltic.

Ring-billed Gull *Larus delawarensis* (Vagrant from North America.)
Following a population explosion in eastern America, this species has become so regular in Britain over the last 20 years or so it has lost its rarity status. It seems only a matter of time before a breeding pair is found in a Common Gull colony – may it be in Sutherland! To date, however, there have been only two records: one at Golspie on 17 February 1982 and an adult at Durness from 22-24 June 1992.

Common Gull *Larus canus* (Common breeding resident, passage migrant and winter visitor.)
Breeding colonies, mostly fairly small, are widely scattered throughout Sutherland in a variety of situations: on offshore islands, moorland, islands in lochs, shingle banks in rivers (where they are particularly vulnerable to flooding) and lowland Mosses. The population appears to be fairly stable, although the annually monitored colony on Clynelish Moss suddenly declined from over 40 pairs in 1991-1995 to only 18 in 1996.

Birds disperse to coasts after the breeding season where they are joined in autumn by immigrants, mainly from Scandinavia and the Baltic. Flocks of up to 250 birds occur at various localities in the south-east in autumn and winter. Most of the non-resident adults leave in March/early April with immature birds following later.

Lesser Black-backed Gull *Larus fuscus* (Breeding summer visitor and passage migrant.)
One of the earliest summer visitors to arrive, the first birds usually appearing in mid March (earliest 14th in the south-east). Formerly much commoner, the species seems never to have recovered from heavy persecution in the late nineteenth century. Numbers are now fairly small, with the majority near north and west coasts (e.g. ten pairs on the Rabbit Islands, Tongue in 1996). A few pairs may breed in the northern peat-

lands and, in the south-east, up to ten pairs nested on Clynelish Moss in the early 1990s, though none bred there in 1996. Other local extinctions, such as on Handa, may reflect a continuing decline in the species' fortunes.

There is surprisingly little evidence of coastal movement in spring, although 11 flew north at Lothbeg Point on 19 May 1996 during a large and unusually late movement of Herring Gulls. Thirty at Loch Brawl on 23 April 1982 probably included local breeders. A more pronounced south-westerly movement occurs in August, maxima 35 (mainly adults) at Brora on 4 August in 1992 and 11 (seven immatures) there on 28 August in 1991. There was a small westerly passage at Strathy Point on 10/11 September 1996.

Herring Gull *Larus argentatus* (Common breeding resident, passage migrant and winter visitor.)

The large increase in the numbers of Herring Gulls breeding in Britain during the second half of this century does not seem to be reflected in Sutherland. Breeding birds are mainly confined to the coasts, the vast majority being in the west. In the late 1960s the population was estimated to be over 6500 pairs but the present total may be somewhat lower. The Handa population declined from 214 pairs in 1981 to only 12 pairs in 1995/96, although an increase in Great Skua numbers may be a factor here. In the south-east, a colony on Clynelish Muir and Moss about 1.6 km, (a mile) from the sea, declined from about 250 pairs in 1991 to only 40 in 1996. After trees were planted on a breeding site north of Loch Fleet in the 1980s, birds continued to nest there in the branches of the young trees for several years.

Flocks of non-breeders feed offshore in summer, with up to 1300 assembling at Loch Fleet. Large movements of this species can occur at almost any time of year, usually into strong south-westerlies. In the south-east, such movements have been observed in early January, late February, early April (450 per hour on 9th in 1993), July, August and October. Spring passage occurs from March to May, with 600 per hour passing Lothbeg Point on 19 May 1996 and up to 1200 per hour coasting north near Helmsdale two days later. The return movement begins in late July – adults were moving south-west through the Clynelish valley at 750 per hour on 31 July 1996 and at least 2500 flew south-west there on 16 August 1995. About 85% of the 1000 which followed this same route on 7 October 1991 were juveniles.

Many local breeders move further south in Britain for the winter. Immigrants at this season are thought to be mainly of north-eastern origin and include birds of the nominate race from Scandinavia, the Baltic and western Russia.

A partially albino immature has been resident in Helmsdale harbour since it arrived (as a juvenile) in summer 1995. It has an unmarked pink bill and pure white primaries, which will no doubt cause increasing confusion as it approaches maturity.

Iceland Gull *Larus glaucoides* (Scarce winter visitor and passage migrant.) One or two Iceland Gulls, usually first year birds and probably originating in eastern Greenland, turn up in harbours in most winters from about mid December onwards. There are sometimes larger influxes, several of which occurred in the early 1980s and another in 1993. For example, there were at least 12 in Achmelvich Bay from 24-27 April 1982. Such arrivals are likely to include birds of the western race *kumleini*, although none has so far been positively identified in Sutherland.

Most records are in the late winter/spring period. Stragglers sometimes remain until late May and there are several June records, most recently a first summer bird at Brora on 1 June 1991. An immature flew north with Kittiwakes there on 12 August 1992. A second year bird which wintered in Helmsdale harbour in 1995/96 was seen again on 8 August 1996 and may have summered in the area.

There are only five recent autumn records: a juvenile at Brora on 10 October 1991, an immature at Strathy Point on 28 October 1984 and first winter birds flying north-east at Lothbeg Point on 27 October 1996 and at Brora on 12 November 1995. A first winter bird had joined the 'resident' third year at Helmsdale on 27 November 1996, both remained into 1997.

The only adults reported in recent years were singles at Kinlochbervie on 5 January 1994, Lochinver on 13 March 1993 and Brora/Golspie between 25 March and 2 April 1983.

Glaucous Gull *Larus hyperboreus* (Winter visitor and passage migrant in small numbers.)

Rather commoner and more predictable in its appearances than Iceland Gull, with records from all coasts. Apart from the odd summering immature, birds do not normally appear before late October/November (mainly in mid to late November). Further arrivals can take place during the winter and numbers reach a peak in April/May, when up to three have been seen together. The majority are first year birds. An adult stayed in the Golspie/Dornoch area from January to April 1985. Birds quite often linger into June and there are odd records from July and September (but not August).

Possible Glaucous x Herring Gull hybrids occurred at Achmelvich in late April 1982 and Loch Fleet in 1993.

Great Black-backed Gull *Larus marinus* (Common breeding resident.)

The largest breeding populations are in the north and west where the current total is probably over 2000 pairs. Numbers on Handa have fluctuated in recent years, with 43 pairs in 1987, 62 pairs in 1989, 27 pairs in 1993 and 33 pairs in 1996. Smaller numbers breed in the south-east from the Ord to Loch Fleet, although an inland colony on an island in Loch Salachaid had over 100 pairs in 1996 and another on Clynelish Moss, Brora, increased to about 80 pairs in the mid 1990s before declining suddenly again to only nine pairs in 1996. Both colonies were apparently unknown during a 1969/70 census.

Large numbers of juveniles pass south through the Moray Firth and off the west coast and west off the north coast after the breeding season. Other coastal movements, involving adults and immatures, seem to relate more to local weather conditions than genuine migration, although 300+ flying north at Lothbeg Point on 19 May in the late spring of 1996 were presumably en route for northern colonies. In the south-east, south-westerly movements have been noted in January/February, April, August and October/November, with at least 600 flying north off Brora on 29 September 1992.

Kittiwake *Rissa tridactyla* (Common breeder, passage migrant, winter visitor.)

Populations of Kittiwakes increased dramatically this century, although some colonies are now declining. In 1969/70 over 17,000 pairs were counted in West Sutherland. The Handa total was then 7000 but this had almost doubled by the mid 1970s. Plot counts have indicated a steady decline there since 1991, but productivity was high at an average of 1.59 fledglings per pair in 1996. There is another large colony on the cliffs at Clo Mor and a number of smaller ones on the north and west coasts, and on offshore islands. Although it does not breed in the south-east, huge numbers from the Caithness colonies feed offshore in summer with thousands resting on the rocks in late summer at Brora and Helmsdale.

Outside the breeding season, movements are very complex and largely weather related. Notable recent passages include over 2000 flying north off Brora on 14 April 1992, at least 10,000 there on 8 September 1994, 1500 per hour moving west off Strathy Point on 27 September 1994, 4000 there on 20 October 1995 and 5000 off Brora on 3 November 1995.

A nestling ringed at Finistere, France in July 1984 was found dead at Melvich that December.

Ivory Gull *Pagophila eburnea* (Vagrant from the High Arctic.)
A second year bird flew north at Brora on 26 March 1992 – a day of frequent wintry showers and a fresh northerly wind. It appeared to come directly from Tarbatness and veered to the north-east, following the line of the coast, as it crossed the Brora rivermouth.

Sandwich Tern *Sterna sandvicensis* (Scarce breeder; common passage migrant in the east.)
A few pairs sometimes nest in Arctic Tern colonies in the south-east. There have also been occasional breeding records from the north-west, where the species is otherwise relatively scarce. At Loch Fleet 40 pairs bred in 1964 but, although successful, the colony was not re-occupied.

The first migrants normally arrive in late March (earliest 22nd), although in some cold springs none appears until the end of the first week of April. Numbers build up through April but most have left by mid May. Family parties are back at Brora and Loch Fleet by mid July.

Only very small numbers occur off the west coast and 40 at the Kyle of Tongue on 16 August 1982 is the highest north coast count. The peak of the autumn passage is late August, maximum 170 at Brora on 28 August 1992. Numbers fall quickly in the second half of September but a few sometimes linger in the south-east until early October.

In the last 25 years the species has shown an increasing tendency to winter in British waters – first in the extreme south but more recently in Scotland, mainly the Firth of Forth. One fishing off Brora on 31 January 1994 was a further reflection of this trend.

Roseate Tern *Sterna dougallii* (Scarce passage migrant, formerly over-looked?)

It seems astonishing that this species was not recorded in Sutherland until 1991. There have now been three sightings, all at Brora: an adult on 7 May 1995, an adult flying north on 18 July and a juvenile, also flying north, on 2 October 1994. As odd pairs of Roseates sometimes nest in Arctic Tern colonies, this is a potential breeder, although the species is much rarer now than earlier in the century.

Common Tern *Sterna hirundo* (Breeding summer visitor and passage migrant.)

Outnumbered by Arctic Terns on the coast, this species also breeds in small colonies on lochs not far from the sea. Less common in the west but a few pairs nest annually on Handa. The largest colony in the south-east is at Loch Fleet where up to 50 pairs breed with varying success. In the north, there were about 60 pairs at Farr Bay on 5 June 1982.

The first birds normally appear in late April (earliest 17th). Post-breeding numbers peak in late July, maxima 87 at the mouth of Loch Fleet on 18 July 1988 and 70 at Handa on 30 July 1985. Very few remain after the end of August but odd passage birds occur in September and October.

Arctic Tern *Sterna paradisaea* (Common breeding summer visitor and passage migrant.)

The arrival of these delightful terns from Antarctica each spring is an annual miracle. Colonies are scattered around all the coasts with possibly the best known occasioning a temporary 'out of bounds' near the ninth green of the Brora golf course. (The Golf Club has adopted the bird as its emblem.) Despite this precaution, the colony has declined from a peak of over 100 pairs in 1992 and was deserted in early summer in both 1995 and 1996. Sutherland's total population, estimated at over 600 pairs in the late 1960s, is probably fairly stable although the species is prone to failure through predation, disturbance and food shortages.

The first birds normally arrive in late April (exceptionally 10th on Handa in 1990). Numbers quickly build up in early May. A count of over 500 at Brora on 14 May 1993 probably included many passage birds. A similar number there on 22 July 1992 included about 150 juveniles.

A steady westward passage of adults off Strathy Point on 24 July 96 illustrates how early many of the northern breeders leave. There were still over 200 at Brora in early August 1993 but relatively few after mid month. Passage birds, presumably from further north, occur throughout September and often well into October. Ten juveniles flew west at Strathy Point on 4 October 1996, followed by 15 on 7 October. Single juveniles also flew west there on 20 October 1995, 21 October 1996 and 1 November 1995, and there was a straggler at Brora until 11 November in 1991.

[Sooty Tern] *Sterna fuscata* (Possible vagrant from tropical oceans.)
One was reported from the mouth of Loch Fleet on 12 September 1986 but the record was not accepted.

Little Tern *Sterna albifrons* (Breeding summer visitor in small numbers.)
The small breeding colonies in the south-east are all subject to increased human disturbance – one of the main factors in nest failure. In recent years, up to 15 pairs have attempted to nest at Brora but none bred there in 1996. Nine pairs have bred at Loch Fleet, which was colonised in the eighties, plus up to five pairs at Dornoch. It has nested in the north in the past but is generally scarce both here and in the west, where the occasional non-breeder reaches Handa.

Normally arrives in early May although there were five at Brora on 30 April 1992. Birds depart soon after breeding and it is scarce by late August.

Black Tern *Chlidonias niger* (Scarce passage migrant.)
Although a regular migrant in southern Britain, this is something of a rarity

in northern Scotland and there are only five records for Sutherland: one flew south-west off Brora on 8 June 1993; two flew north there on 19 June 1992; one at the mouth of the River Naver on 5 July 1973; one flew north at Brora on 11 August 1996; one at the Brora rivermouth on 28/29 August 1992 was joined by a second bird on 30 August.

Guillemot *Uria aalge* (Common breeder in north-west and west, passage migrant and winter visitor.)
Sutherland holds over 10% of the increasing Scottish breeding population on its north and west coasts with something in excess of 100,000 pairs. Over half of these are on Handa where a count of 120,000 birds was made in 1994 (Stoneman et al 1995). About 10% are of the bridled form. A leucistic individual has returned there each year since 1993. Plot counts indicated another slight increase in 1996 when productivity was averaging 0.76 chicks per pair. Colonies are occupied in late winter with large westward movements off the north coast in April probably comprising both new arrivals and feeding birds.

Post-breeding dispersal is complex with many birds leaving for Scandinavian waters and the North Sea. In the Moray Firth, numbers build up during the autumn and onshore winds can produce spectacular flights: at least 5000 flew north off Brora on 9 October 1991 and 3000 passed there on 3 November 1993.

Winter numbers are much smaller. At Lothbeg Point 200 flew north on 27 January 1996. Prolonged stormy weather can result in 'wrecks' such as that in February 1994 when hundreds were washed up on eastern beaches. Another large mortality occurred in early 1996.

Brünnich's Guillemot *Uria lomvia* (Rare winter visitor from the Arctic, probably overlooked.)
A freshly dead bird was found at Sputie Burn, south of Brora, on 3 February 1982 and another at Golspie on 24 December 1982.

During the severe winter of 1995/96, which brought unprecedented numbers of Little Auks into the Moray Firth, the author had unsatisfactory views of two possible Brünnich's in late December/early January and then a close flight view of a dense black, heavily built bird with deep wing beats, in dark-headed 'funereal' garb, at Lothbeg Point on 12 January 1996*. An identical bird flew north there on 18 December 1996* during another big Little Auk movement.

Razorbill *Alca torda* (Common breeder in north-west and west, passage migrant and winter visitor.)

Like the Guillemot, Scottish populations seem to have increased over the last 30 years and the Sutherland total is now likely to be in excess of 20,000 pairs of which almost half are on Handa. Over 16,000 individuals were counted there in 1987, making the colony the largest in the British Isles with over 9% of the population (Lloyd et al 1991). Some birds return to colonies as early as February.

Large late winter and spring movements off the north and east coasts include 1500 flying south off Brora in an hour on 24 February 1992, 1500 flying north there on 28 March 1993 and 2 and 9 April 1995 and over 1000 flying west at Strathy Point on 7 April 1995.

After the breeding season Razorbills complete their moult before Guillemots but it is into September before any sizeable movements occur in the Moray Firth. At least 800 flew north off Brora on 11 September 1992 and at least 1000 passed there on 15 September 1994. About 1000 per hour flew west at Strathy Point on 27 September 1994. Autumn numbers peak in October, maxima several thousand off Brora on 2 October 1994, 1000 per hour there on 19 October 1994 and 5000 on 24 October 1995. Flights of over 1000 continue into early November but early winter numbers are much smaller, although 200 per hour flew north at Lothbeg Point on 27 January 1996.

This species is less prone to 'wrecks' than Guillemot. In the exceptionally cold winter of 1947 a bird of the northern race *torda* was found dead at Brora on 12 March.

Black Guillemot *Cepphus grylle* (Resident, breeding mainly in the north and west.)

Sutherland has an apparently stable breeding population of around 500 pairs. On the east coast it has the merest toehold just south of the Ord of Caithness. The species has not bred on Handa since 1978 although it still nests nearby. A rat eradication project will hopefully encourage its return.

'Tysties' are certainly not 'scarce winter visitors to the east coast', as described by Angus (1983). Regular sea-watching at Brora has shown they occur in every month with peaks in late March, September/October and late December. The largest recent northward movements there occurred on 23 and 30 March 1992 (14), 9 September 1993 (24), 13 October 1996 (14), 28 October 1992 (17) and 25 December 1995 (17).

Black Guillemots at Brora, 1990-1996

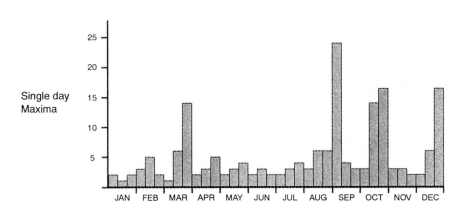

Little Auk *Alle alle* (Winter visitor in variable numbers.)
Little Auks breed in huge colonies in the High Arctic. In some winters few reach Scottish waters but good years have increased in frequency in line with a southerly shift in their winter distribution (attributable to the cooling of Arctic regions over the last half century). The largest numbers are seen in the Moray Firth, but the species also moves through the Pentland Firth and occurs off the west coast. Occasional 'wrecks' deposit dead and dying birds on beaches and sometimes well inland.

The earliest record is of one at Brora on 1 October 1994. A few are usually offshore in the second half of October, typically 15 flying west off Strathy Point on 21 October 1996. Fifty-eight flew north-east at Lothbeg Point on 28 October 1996 and 65 passed Brora in an hour on 4 November 1996. Larger movements tend to occur from December to February. There were unprecedented numbers in the Moray Firth in winter

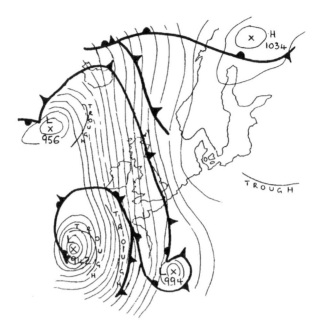

Synoptic chart for 06.00 GMT on 7 January 1996. A deep depression in the south-west approaches, gale force south-easterly winds over northern Scotland, and parallel cold fronts in the northern North Sea combined to drive thousands of Little Auks into the Moray Firth.

1995/96. The first big movement occurred on 11 November when 327 flew north-east off Brora, followed by 302 on 26 November. On Christmas Day, to the detriment of the catering arrangements, 1670 were counted at Brora in three hours. Hogmanay was also disrupted by flights of 122 on 31 December and 508 on 1 January. Then, in a strong south-easterly, over 3000 passed Lothbeg Point on 6 January followed by at least 6500 the following day.

Numbers were also high in early winter 1996/97, with 528 passing Lothbeg Point on 18 December 1996.

The largest February movement was of 58 flying south off Brora on 3rd. in 1995. There have been no recent records between 18 February and 12 May, when one flew south-west off Brora ahead of a cold front in 1993. One was picked up in Dornoch on 14 June 1962 and there was one at Achmelvich on 31 July 1979.

[Crested Auklet] *Aethia cristatella* (Possible vagrant from the North Pacific.) Apart from a Parakeet Auklet, which was found on a lake in Sweden after extreme weather in 1860, the only historical record of a pacific auk in European waters was of a Crested Auklet 'collected' off north-east Iceland in August 1912. Recently, however there has been an Ancient Murrelet on Lundy, a Tufted Puffin in Sweden and, most recently…

Iain MacDonald was sea-watching off Brora in August 1994 when he picked up a small all-dark auk just over a kilometre (0.75 miles) offshore. It landed on the choppy sea and that was the last he saw of it. On 18 January 1995, after the third severe gale in five days, I was watching at the same locality in razor-sharp light when I spotted a small, plump all-dark bird with a fast, low but erratic flight flying south. From the size, Crested Auklet appears to be the only possibility. Astonishingly, on 26 November 1995, during a large passage of Little Auks, an identical bird flew north-east at Brora – much closer than the first but in poor light which rendered any subtle plumage characteristics invisible. The pot-bellied shape, 'bill-less' profile, erratic flight and size (only slightly larger than Little Auk) again point to Crested Auklet.

Why, then, this sudden glut of pacific auklets? Two possibilities spring to mind. First, perhaps 'normal' Arctic weather patterns have been disrupted by recent climatic changes. Birds caught up in storms would not have to be displaced far for their southward migration to carry them into the North Atlantic rather than the North Pacific. (Circumpolar distances at very high latitudes are not great in ornithological terms.) Crested Auklet, as the northernmost breeder of the pacific auks, would, on this scenario, be the most likely species to be displaced. A second possibility involves recent overlapping of the ranges of the high Arctic pacific auks with Little Auk, which seems to have extended its summer range into the North Pacific. If these Little Auks return to the North Atlantic in winter they may bring the odd pacific auklet back with them. Whatever the reason, the fascination of sea-watching off Sutherland's coasts is further enhanced.

Puffin *Fratercula arctica* (Breeding summer visitor. Winters at sea, but occasionally driven onto coasts.)
Sutherland boasts the largest mainland colony of Puffins in Britain –

Clo Mor is thought to hold more than 50,000 pairs although accurate censuses are impossible. The Handa population, whilst relatively small, is regularly monitored. Whole island counts increased from 300 in 1989 to over 1000 in 1990 (Stoneman *et al* 1995) and a record 1214 was counted in July 1996. Colonies are re-occupied in late March and abandoned in August, although many birds are still visible from coasts in early September.

Although Puffins do not breed in the south-east, birds from further north feed in the Moray Firth and counts of over 100 off Brora are fairly regular in summer. Autumn movements are smaller and a few are seen intermittently from late September through to early January, maximum eight off Brora on 1 January 1991. There are no recent records for late January, February or early/mid March.

Pallas's Sandgrouse *Syrrhaptes paradoxus* (Vagrant from central Asia.)
This Asiatic steppe species used to irrupt fairly frequently up to the late nineteenth century, reaching western Europe in some numbers and even staying on to breed. One was shot at Dornoch on 6 June 1863, when others occurred in Caithness.

Rock Dove *Columba livia* (Breeding resident.)
The status of 'pure' Rock Doves is obscured by long-term interbreeding with feral pigeons. More or less pure populations still exist on the north and west coasts. Although mainly sedentary, autumn flocks may include some immigrants since migration is regularly noted in the Northern Isles.

Stock Dove *Columba oenas* (Formerly a scarce breeder; now rare.)
Stock Doves colonised Scotland from the south in the second half of the nineteenth century, first breeding in 1866 but not reaching the Moray Firth until 1885. In Sutherland their breeding range was restricted to the south-east although there were occasional sightings in the north and west. Breeding continued until the 1980s. A pair raised two young near Loch Fleet in 1985, where the species was still present in June 1990. More recent records are all of passage birds: three near Brora on 16 April 1993, two there on 26 September 1992 and one on 23 October 1991, all flying south-west.

Woodpigeon *Columba palumbus* (Breeding resident and passage migrant.)
A common resident in the south-east and north, Woodpigeons appear to be mainly summer visitors in the west, where they are nowhere common.

South-westerly movements, usually of less than 100 birds, along the east coast fly-way have been noted in January and February (maxima 179 on 2 February and over 300 on 22 February 1992) and from October to December.

Collared Dove *Streptopelia decaocto* (Breeding resident.)
The amazing spread of the Collared Dove across Europe from the Near East from about 1930 is well documented. In Britain, it first bred in Norfolk in 1955 and reached Moray only two years later. It first occurred in Sutherland in 1964, bred in 1966, and is now well established throughout the populated parts of the county. Numbers are still increasing in places, with some spread from villages to outlying settlements.

Not surprisingly for a bird spreading north-west, migrants are regularly seen on offshore islands such as Handa, mainly in spring.

Turtle Dove *Streptopelia turtur* (Scarce passage migrant.)
This southern, migratory dove has been reported in only six of the last 15 years: one at Bettyhill on 12 May 1990, one at Dornoch on 16 May 1996, one at Keoldale, Kyle of Durness, on 28 May 1988, one on Handa on 2 June 1982, one at Borrobol on 2 June 96, one at Dornoch on 5 August 1983, one at Strathy Point from 7-17 October 1988 and one with Collared Doves in Brora on 11 November 1993.

Cuckoo *Cuculus canorus* (Breeding summer resident.)
Cuckoos take full advantage of the large, widespread Meadow Pipit populations, but there seems to have been a decline in the numbers reaching the north coast in recent years. The first birds normally arrive in late April. One at Achnabourin on 9 April 1992 was exceptionally early. Breeding density can be high in favourable places, e.g. up to five females on Ferry Links, Loch Fleet. Adults leave the breeding grounds from about mid July and the few August records are mainly of juveniles.

Barn Owl *Tyto alba* (Scarce breeding resident.)
A few pairs breed in the south-east, where it has recently been seen as far north as Portgower. A pair successfully reared one chick at Lothbeg in 1996 – at present the most northerly pair in the world! In the nineteenth century, it bred at Rosehall, in the north (Tongue) and the west (Loch Assynt), but there are no recent records from any of these areas.

Scops Owl *Otus scops* (Vagrant from southern Europe.)
One was shot at Morvich, near Golspie, in May 1854.

Snowy Owl *Nyctea scandiaca* (Rare winter visitor and passage migrant.)
Harvie-Brown and Buckley (1887) list three records from the nineteenth century, including one obtained at Altnaharra in October 1853. In recent times one at Whiten Head on 13 April 1972 and one south of Strathy in mid-September 1993 are the only confirmed sightings, although there is a report of one on Ben Klibreck in winter 1994/95.

Tawny Owl *Strix aluco* (Breeding resident.)
Tawny Owls are commonest in the more heavily wooded and populous south-east but they also occur sparingly in the west and north, where three pairs bred within 500 yards at one locality in 1985. The population seems to be fairly stable.

Normally considered sedentary, one ringed as a nestling at Torbol on 4 May 1987 was found dead on a road in Dyfed that November (possibly killed nearer home and transported by the offending vehicle). One on Handa on 5 September 1990 is also a surprising record.

Long-eared Owl *Asio otus* (Breeding resident and passage migrant.)
This species occupies a variety of habitats throughout the county, needing only scrub or a small plantation for nesting. It is under-recorded because of its strictly nocturnal habits and is almost certainly Sutherland's most numerous owl.

Migrants, probably from Scandinavia, occur in autumn, e.g. one flying south-west over the sea at Brora on 13 October 1991.

Short-eared Owl *Asio flammeus* (Scarce breeding summer visitor and passage migrant; rare in winter.)
Given the amount of apparently suitable habitat available, particularly in the form of young plantations, it is surprising this graceful and relatively conspicuous owl remains scarce in Sutherland. Up to nine birds could be seen in the early summer of 1972 during the early growth of the Shin Forest. A few pairs still breed in the south-east and in north/central areas; elsewhere it seems to be only a passage migrant. Most birds are seen on autumn passage with a peak in late August. There are a few winter records from all coasts.

[Tengmalm's Owl] *Aegolius funereus* (Possible vagrant from Fenno-Scandinavia.)
Harvie-Brown and Buckley (1887) refer to a bird killed at Spinningdale in May 1847 but they could find no trace of the specimen. Although the date seems a little unlikely, one recent Orkney record was on 1 May. This species is irruptive in northern Europe and occasionally reaches Scotland (mainly the Northern Isles) in late autumn and winter, so it is likely to occur again sooner or later. The only problem is finding one!

Nightjar *Caprimulgus europaeus* (Former breeder; now very scarce.)
In the nineteenth century Nightjars bred in the south-east, the west and north to Loch Eriboll. The species' range contracted during the twentieth century although it bred sparingly in south-east Sutherland until the early 1970s. Only one singing male was located in 1981 and one was reported in May 1995 from Scourie.

Swift *Apus apus* (Breeding summer visitor and passage migrant.)
As a breeding bird the Swift is confined to southern and central Sutherland. It normally arrives in the second week of May. One at Lairg on 11 April 1984 was exceptionally early. Most have left by mid August. Occasional migrants are seen into September/October and, in 1982, there was even one in Golspie on 1 November. That autumn unprecedented numbers lingered at Dornoch, where there were 80 on 10 September, followed by ones and twos elsewhere up to 14 October.

Small numbers occasionally reach the north coast in late May and June. Numbers on Handa tend to peak in the range 15-20 in July and August.

[Pallid Swift] *Apus pallidus* (Possible vagrant from southern Europe.)
One was reported from Handa on 5 May 1984 but the record was not accepted as proven.

Alpine Swift *Apus melba* (Vagrant from southern Europe.)
One at Clo Mor on 21 July 1992 is the only record.

Kingfisher *Alcedo atthis* (Scarce passage migrant.)
Although Kingfishers have bred as near as the River Ness in recent years, those occurring in Sutherland (all but one in autumn) are presumably migrants from southern Scandinavia or the Baltic region. Angus (1983) listed five records (of four birds) from 1962-1982, all between 24 September and 26 November. Since then there have been only two further sightings: one at Little Loch Shin, Lairg on 28 January 1993 and one at Lower Brora on 10 August 1995. The latter, a young male, was found on the coastal path with a broken wing.

Bee-eater *Merops apiaster* (Rare passage migrant.)
This exotic migrant from the Mediterranean region has occurred on four or five occasions since 1935: one at Durness from 2-4 May 1966, one near Achmelvich on 31 May 1988, presumably the same bird at Loch Hope on 2 June 1988, one flying south over Ferry Links, Loch Fleet on 20 July 1988 (possibly the same again), one in Strath Halladale on 14 August 1959 and one at Loth on 12 September 1935.

Roller *Coracias garrulus* (Vagrant from southern Europe.)
One at Ledmore on 7 June 1979 is the only record.

Hoopoe *Upupa epops* (Scarce passage migrant.)
Unlike most other scarce migrants, Hoopoes are usually reported, even by non-birders, so the available records of this overshooter from the Continent are probably a fairly true reflection of its status. In spring, the

earliest was one at Achfary on 20 April 1985. It occurred twice in early May in the early 1970s, at Loch Choire and Loth, and one was reported from Kildonan in late May 1985.

All other recent records are in autumn, and include three or four birds in 1993: one at Rosehall on 13 September 1993, one at Bighouse in October 1974, one at Dornoch on 3 October 1965, one at Achnalochy, near Skelpick on 3 October 1988, one west of Bonar Bridge on 11 October 1993, possibly the same bird in Strath Carron from 12-15 October 1993 and one at Brora and Kintradwell on 22 October 1993.

Wryneck *Jynx torquilla* (Scarce summer visitor and passage migrant.)
As the Wryneck neared extinction as an English breeding bird in the 1960s, a new population (presumably of Scandinavian origin) became tenuously established in the Highlands. This expansion was reflected in records from Loch Hope in May/June 1969 (a singing male), Glencassley on 31 May 1971, Altnaharra on 6 May 1975 and Dallangwell on 21 May 1978. There were then 13 blank years before one sang in the author's garden early on 12 June 1992. One at Forsinard in late May 1996 occurred during a large fall of Scandinavia-bound migrants.

A few might be expected in 'drift' conditions in late August/September but the only autumn record is of one between Embo and Dornoch on 3 September 1958.

[Green Woodpecker] *Picus viridis* (One specimen of uncertain origin; a potential colonist.)
Harvie-Brown and Buckley (1887) refer to a bird in the Dunrobin Museum marked 'Bonar 1848'. In the last 50 years the species has been spreading north and had reached both Easter and Wester Ross by the mid 1970s. It is therefore slightly surprising that none has yet been definitely seen in Sutherland although there have been recent unconfirmed reports from north of Lairg, the Golspie area and the south-facing oakwood at Spinningdale, which seems the most likely locality.

Great Spotted Woodpecker *Dendrocopus major* (Breeding resident and scarce passage migrant.)
After becoming extinct as a breeding bird in Scotland during the nineteenth century, this woodpecker spread north again as far as Sutherland in the first half of the twentieth century. Nowhere common, the species is now thinly distributed through the south-east and south and also breeds very locally in the north and west.

Migrants of the nominate Scandinavian and Continental race sometimes occur in autumn, such as the very tame bird in Dornoch in November/December 1962. There are occasional irruptions, as in 1862, when birds were 'very abundant' in the east, being shot even on Ben Klibreck! More recently, there was a smaller arrival in 1974. One flying south-west through the Clynelish valley, Brora, with migrating thrushes on 29 October 1993 was almost certainly of this race.

[Short-toed Lark] *Calandrella cinerea* (Possible vagrant from southern Europe and western Asia.)
This regular migrant to the Northern Isles was reported from Culkein,

Drumbeg on 12 June 1990 but the record was not accepted.

Skylark *Alauda arvensis* (Breeding summer visitor, arriving early spring; scarce or very local in winter.)
Skylarks return to lowland areas in the second half of February, when the odd singing bird may be heard. At least 100 came in from the east at Brora on 27 February 1993 and a flock of 27 flew west through the Clynelish valley on 24 March 1993.

Upland breeding territories are occupied as soon as the weather permits. The species is widespread during the summer with the highest densities in coastal areas and the lower hills. On the 'flows', numbers are generally small. In the west, the population on the island of Handa has fluctuated between 25 pairs (1982) and 49 pairs (1991); in the south-east more than 50 pairs usually nest around Loch Fleet.

Autumn movements are less obvious but small numbers have been seen flying south-west at Brora, maxima 13 on 8 October 1994, a total of 15 on 7/8 October 1995 and 13 on 1 November 1993. Winter records away from the extreme south-east are normally associated with hard weather, such as the small southerly movement at Brora on 27 December 1995.

Shore Lark *Eremophila alpestris* (Scarce passage migrant and winter visitor.)
This species' normal migration route takes them well to the east and south of Sutherland. It was first recorded as recently as 1976/77, when three wintered at Littleferry, Loch Fleet from 19 December until 19 March. This was a time of exceptional numbers in Scotland which led to at least one instance of successful breeding in the Highlands.

Since then there have been two early autumn records of migrants: three on ploughed land near Dornoch on 3 September 1995 and two on the beach at Brora on 13 September 1992.

Sand Martin *Riparia riparia* (Breeding summer visitor and passage migrant.)
Small breeding colonies are scattered throughout the county, although the species is commoner in the south-east. It is now recovering well from the

the population crash of the late 1960s (caused by the Sahel drought) and may be back to near-optimum numbers. The year 1996 was certainly a bumper year with an exceptionally large arrival in late April. Numbers feeding over Loch Brora in cool weather rose to a record 520 on 28 April and 120 were feeding over tidal rocks at Brora on 17 May.

The first arrivals are much later than in southern Britain – usually in mid April (earliest 30 March). Feeding flocks build up away from the colonies in late summer. Most have left by late August. Later birds (latest 17 September) are probably migrants from elsewhere.

Swallow *Hirundo rustica* (Breeding summer visitor and passage migrant.)
Swallows are widespread but commonest in the south-east. A pair nested on Eilean nan Ron in 1992, raising five young.

They normally arrive in mid or late April (earliest 2nd). Flocks of up to 100 build up at Brora and Loch Fleet in August. South-westerly movements of passage birds along the east coast fly-way occur in September. Odd birds often remain into October and there are three recent November records (latest 24th).

House Martin *Delichon urbica* (Breeding summer visitor and passage migrant.)
Fairly widespread in small numbers in the south-east, House Martins become increasingly local to the west and north. One or two pairs still occasionally breed 'naturally' in Smoo Cave, where it was described as common in the early nineteenth century.

This is usually the latest of the hirundines to arrive, birds sometimes not appearing until May (earliest 10 April). In 1995 the main influx was as late as 23 May.

Sightings away from the breeding colonies are infrequent and usually involve very small numbers. Most of the few records from Handa are in June. Flocks of up to 50 birds form in the south-east from late July, with at least this number at Culrain on 26 September 1985. A few often linger into early October and there are two recent November records: one at Golspie on 5 November 1982 and two at Durness on 8 November 1994. Two remained in Dornoch until 15 November 1945.

First and last dates for hirundines in Sutherland

	Earliest	Latest
Sand Martin	30 March	17 September
Swallow	2 April	24 November
House Martin	10 April	15 November

Tree Pipit *Anthus trivialis* (Breeding summer visitor and passage migrant.) This migrant pipit expanded its range in the first half of the twentieth century and is now thinly but widely distributed, breeding wherever there are suitable open woods. The first birds normally arrive in late April but there was an exceptionally early one at Loch Brora on 9 April 1996.

This species figures in any 'falls' of Scandinavia-bound migrants in spring, as in May 1985, when unusual numbers passed through the Melvich area, and in late May 1996 when there was a sprinkling of birds along the north and east coasts from 20th, with new arrivals dropping in from the east at Helmsdale and Brora on 26th.

Few birds are seen after the end of August but a few migrants occur in September, again usually associated with 'drift' migration from the east.

Meadow Pipit *Anthus pratensis* (Breeding summer visitor in large numbers and passage migrant; scarce except in the mildest winters.) This is undoubtedly Sutherland's commonest bird during the summer months. All but the highest breeding territories are normally re-occupied by late March/early April. Late snow can result in large concentrations in the lower straths, such as one of several hundreds by Loch Brora on 17 April 1995.

Flocks also form after the breeding season and large movements of migrants can occur in autumn, e.g. several hundreds flying south-west at Brora on the early morning of 6 October 1991. Good numbers remain in the hills and in the milder west until the first winter frosts bite. Small hard weather movements result from mid winter cold snaps, but by this time most of 'our' birds are thought to be in south-west Europe, mainly Iberia.

Rock Pipit *Anthus petrosus* (Breeding resident, mainly in the north and west; winter visitor to the south-east.)
Apart from a few pairs on the east coast to the north of Helmsdale, the large breeding population is distributed fairly generally along the coasts and on the islands of the north and west. Around 20-35 pairs breed on Handa.

On 1 October 1996, a total of eight arrived at Strathy Point from Hoy, three of which then circled high and returned north.

South of Helmsdale, the first birds appear in early September and remain until about mid April, sometimes gathering on beaches in loose flocks of up to 25 birds in hard weather. In the north, about 100 assembled on Melvich beach on 28 December 1985.

Water Pipit *Anthus spinoletta* (Rare passage migrant, possibly overlooked.)
There are relatively few records of this species (formerly regarded as a race of the Rock Pipit) in Scotland, but considerable numbers now winter annually in England and 'overshooters' must occur more often than they are reported. Any Rock-type Pipit inland or beside freshwater should be examined closely. To the experienced ear, the call is quite distinct from Rock Pipit's, being fuller, slightly lower pitched and more confident. The only record is of one flying south-west through the Clynelish valley, Brora on 23 October 1996, calling repeatedly.

Yellow Wagtail *Motacilla flava* (Scarce passage migrant.)
As a regular Scottish breeding bird the Yellow Wagtail *M. f. flavissima* is confined to the south-west, although there are sporadic attempts to nest further north and east. In the far north, migrants are more likely to belong to one of the Continental races, particularly Blue-headed *M. f. flava*.

Most of the records are in May and all but one of the spring birds were male: one *flava* on Handa in early May 1983, one *flavissima* at Balnakeil from 9-19 May 1983; one (claimed as *feldegg* but not accepted as such) on Handa on 12 May 1982, one *flavissima*) at Strathy on 18 May 1974, one *flava* at Balnakeil on 19 May 1973, one *flava* at Loth on 22 May 1996, one female (race undetermined) at Balnakeil on 26 May 1985, one (claimed as *feldegg* but again not accepted) at Forsinard on 27 May 1995 and one *thunbergi* at Balnakeil on 28 May 1995. Single *flava* occurred on Handa on 1 June 1985 and 15 June 1987.

One flying south-west through the Clynelish valley, Brora on 4 October 1992 (calling) is, rather surprisingly, the only autumn record.

Grey Wagtail *Motacilla cinerea* (Breeding summer visitor and passage migrant; a few overwinter in the extreme south-east.)
The main arrival takes place from mid March to early April and breeding territories are occupied almost immediately. The species is fairly common and widely distributed except for the north-west, where many suitable rivers and burns are untenanted.

Some south-westerly movement along the east coast fly-way is apparent from late August to October but numbers are small (maximum five on 24 August 1996). Most birds are thought to move to southern Britain but a few remain near the south-east coast in all but the hardest winters.

Pied Wagtail *Motacilla alba* (Abundant breeding summer visitor and passage migrant; a few over winter most years.)
The British breeding race *yarrelli* winters further south in Britain and on the Continent, returning to Sutherland in the second half of March and April. It is double brooded in good summers and post-breeding flocks build up in July and August. Over 100 were feeding around the Brora rivermouth on 22 August and there were at least 70 in one field by Loch Brora on 29 August 1996.

South-westerly passage along the east coast fly-way occurs mainly in October, e.g. 32 at Brora early on 6 October 1991. Numbers from November to February are small, with a complete exodus in hard winters.

The White Wagtail *M. a. alba* is a passage migrant in small numbers although the odd pair has bred. In spring, birds occur mainly from late April to mid May (earliest 14 April). Sixteen on Handa on 19 April 1987 and 20 at Balnakeil on 15/16 May 1995 are the highest counts. In autumn the proportion of White to Pied is harder to determine, but there were nine on Handa on 5 September 1987 and eight at Dornoch on 14 September 1985.

Waxwing *Bombycilla garrulus* (Occasional irruptive winter visitor and passage migrant; one spring and one summer record.)
Three flying east through the Clynelish valley, Brora on 14 October 1996 is the earliest autumn record.

Invasions of Waxwings from Fenno-Scandinavia and Russia enliven all too few winters. The main beneficiaries are usually the eastern coastal villages but birds occur more widely in the bigger irruptions. In recent years, there was a small arrival in November 1985, with two remaining at Ardgay until 6 April 1986, 20 at Lochinver on 27 October 1988, 12 at Melvich on 21 October 1990, 18 in Golspie on 6 November 1990, 50 at Balnakeil on 31 October and 33 at West Clyne, Brora on 22 November 1991 and over 20 in Golspie in late January 1996.

One remained in Dornoch from 22 April to 1 May 1966. The most surprising record is of a bird at Corriemulzie on 29 June 1973.

Dipper *Cinclus cinclus* (Breeding resident.)
Dippers are fairly common along suitable rivers and burns throughout the county. Although numbers fluctuate, there is no evidence of any overall decline in the population. In winter, they move down to the lower straths and coastal areas where they are well capable of surviving the hardest weather. At such times several may be seen together in a short stretch of river.

Wren *Troglodytes troglodytes* (Abundant and widespread breeding resident.)
Wrens occupy a wide variety of habitats at all but the highest altitudes. They were particularly common after a series of mild winters in the late 1980s and early 1990s but their numbers were drastically reduced by the exceptionally low temperatures of late December 1995 (down to -27 °C, -16.6 °F over parts of the county). Barring a mini ice-age, numbers will no doubt soon be back to normal.

Dunnock *Prunella modularis* (Common and widespread breeding resident, passage migrant and winter immigrant.)

Dunnocks breed wherever sufficient vegetative cover exists, but are absent from the higher mountains, tree-less 'flows' and offshore islands.

Although the species is often disregarded as a passage migrant, the Scandinavian and east Baltic populations are migratory and this race can occur in some numbers on the Northern Isles, and presumably therefore in Sutherland. Some Continental birds probably also winter here.

Robin *Erithacus rubecula* (Common breeding resident and passage migrant.)
The familiar ever-present garden Robin disguises the species' more complex status. As a breeding bird it is widespread in lowland and hill areas with some woodland or shrub cover. The extent to which it has benefited from new plantations has not been assessed.

Migrants of the nominate Continental race pass through Sutherland mainly in autumn, although there were up to 13 on Handa in early May 1982. Peak passage is in late September/October with some birds probably overwintering. Prolonged hard weather undoubtedly has an effect on the size of the resident population. At such times, numbers of Robins resort to the tide-wrack on beaches as well as bird tables.

Bluethroat *Luscinia svecica* (Scarce passage migrant.)
This is one of those regular passage migrants to the Northern Isles that, until recently, was conspicuous only by its absence in Sutherland. The first county records were in 1985, when there was one on Handa from 20-22 May, one sang for about two weeks in June in the west and there was another near Ben More Lodge on 16 June. Since then there have been four more sightings: singles on Handa on 25 May 1987, north of Helmsdale (singing) on 26 May 1996 (during a large arrival of Continental migrants), near Loch Buidhe on 8 June 1995 and at Rhiconnich on 9 June 1991. All were males of the red-spotted form.

Black Redstart *Phoenicurus ochruros* (Scarce passage migrant.)
Although this species was not included in *Sutherland Birds* (1983), the first county record was of one at Embo Street on 12 October 1978. A female was seen at Brora on 14 April 1985 but there were then no further

sightings (apart from a claimed female Redstart on Handa on 1 April 1989 – see below) until 1996 when, during a large 'fall' of Continental migrants, at least four were reported from 21-28 May: three or four, including one male, between Portgower and Brora and one female by Loch Eriboll on 27 May.

Redstart *Phoenicurus phoenicurus* (Breeding summer visitor, passage migrant.) Commonest in the south and south-east, Redstarts breed locally wherever there is mature broad-leaved or open pine woodland. Numbers fluctuate from year to year but the last bumper season was as long ago as 1982. The loss of birch woodland through lack of regeneration is a threat to the species' longer term status. Breeding territories are occupied by males from late April. The main arrival is in early May. Post-breeding dispersal takes young birds into fringe habitats, including gardens in rural areas. Most have departed by mid August.

The earliest reported arrival was on Handa on the exceptional date of 1 April 1989. As this was a female, the possibility of confusion with Black Redstart (a much earlier migrant) has to be considered. Two males at Achentoul on 5 April 1996 were otherwise the earliest. 'Falls' of Continental migrants in spring and autumn sometimes includes large numbers of Redstarts. Such an event occurred in late May 1996, when birds were scattered mainly along the east coast, and in mid September 1995, when persistent strong easterlies deposited birds throughout the county. Harvie-Brown and Buckley (1887) describe a similar arrival from 8-10 October 1863.

Whinchat *Saxicola rubetra* (Breeding summer visitor, passage migrant.) Fairly common and widely distributed, Whinchats are one of the principal beneficiaries of the spread of young plantations. The first birds normally arrive in late April or early May (exceptionally 7 April in 1985). There were nine on Handa on 14 May 1982, where only a few migrants normally occur. A good sprinkling of migrants arrived, mainly in the east, during classic 'fall' conditions between 20 and 27 May 1996.

The drift south begins as soon as the breeding season is over. In recent years none has been seen later than mid September.

Stonechat *Saxicola torquata* (Widespread breeding resident, retreating to coastal areas in winter.)

Stonechat numbers fluctuate markedly in relation to the severity of the winters. A succession of mild winters in the late 1980s and early 1990s allowed an abnormally high population to build up. Numbers crashed after an exceptionally cold spell in late December 1995. Pairs were very hard to find in the east in 1996, although two fully fledged juveniles accompanied a female on Clynelish Moss as early as 26 May. Mortality was probably lower near the west and north coasts.

Inland territories are occupied from late March or early April. Family parties remain together during the summer. Larger concentrations are normally associated with hard weather, when loose flocks of up to 12 may congregate on beaches.

Wheatear *Oenanthe oenanthe* (Common breeding resident and passage migrant.)

Despite this species' recent tendency to arrive earlier in southern Britain, the first birds do not reach Sutherland until late March (earliest 22nd) or, more usually, early April. The main arrivals are in mid to late April, after which it is widely distributed from coasts to all but the highest tops.

Breeding densities are highest in well-grazed areas. Around 35 pairs nest on Handa. Local birds disperse after breeding and drift south in August.

Migrant Wheatears fall into two categories: the distinctive northern breeding *leucorrhoa* ('Greenland' Wheatear), which tends to pass through in May and September/October (one at Handa on 29 August 1985 was unusually early), and birds from Continental populations of the nominate race, the presence of which can only be assumed during 'falls' in spring and autumn. Stragglers rarely occur into November (latest one at Moine on 11 November 1983).

White's Thrush *Zoothera dauma* (Vagrant from Siberia.)
One at East Clyne, Brora from 27-29 September 1991 may have been present for several days previously, according to the crofter.

Ring Ouzel *Turdus torquatus* (Declining breeding summer visitor and scarce passage migrant.)
This was a common breeding bird in the nineteenth century but the population declined steadily during the first half of the twentieth century and is still declining today. However, it is always likely to be under-recorded given the remoteness of much of its favourite habitat. A few localities, such as Strath Carron in the extreme south, continue to hold several pairs. The first birds normally arrive in early April. One near Loch Hope on 13 March 1993 is by far the earliest. A migrant at Loch Brora on 24 May 1996, associated with a large 'fall', was probably Scandinavia-bound.

In autumn, odd birds come in from Scandinavia with the 'winter' thrushes in October. Juveniles occurred at East Clyne, Brora on 5 October 1991 and Melvich on 17 October 1996 and an adult male flew south-west through the Clynelish valley on 20 October 1991. There are November records from Brora and Loch Hope.

Blackbird *Turdus merula* (Breeding resident, passage migrant and winter immigrant.)
Blackbirds are common along the coasts, around settlements and in the better wooded lowland areas of the interior. Most breeders appear to be resident but ringing returns suggest some young birds move south-west,

mainly to Ireland, for the winter, when they are replaced by immigrants from Fenno-Scandinavia.

Spring passage is hard to detect. However, four birds ringed at Golspie in winter have been recovered in Norway and Sweden in spring/summer. Autumn passage/ immigration begins in September and peaks in October/November, when flocks are sometimes seen at higher altitudes.

Fieldfare *Turdus pilaris* (Occasional breeder; mainly autumn passage migrant with some overwintering in milder years.)
Two near Altnaharra in July 1982, a pair carrying food at Dalreavoch on 2 June and a singing male at Loch Naver in 1983, one carrying food at Dalnamain on 3 July 1984 and a nest near Loth in 1990 are the most recent breeding records.

In autumn, birds have been recorded from 15 September. The main arrival takes place in October/November (late September in 1985). Recent counts on the east coast fly-way include at least 4500 on 24 October 1996 and 1150 on 4 November 1994. Most pass straight through, but small numbers linger into the New Year, and beyond in mild winters. Exceptions were the winters of 1987/88, when there were up to 200 at Strathy in January and 2000 at Armadale on 6 March, and 1995/96, when very low temperatures in late December brought a new influx. There were over 350 in the Brora area on 1 January, over 500 flew south west there on 25 January and flocks totalling several thousands were scattered throughout the south east on 30 January. Most had disappeared by early March.

Spring passage is comparatively slight and sometimes negligible. There were 20 in Glen Loth on 29 April 1993 and odd birds occur widely into May (latest on Handa on 26 May 1985).

Song Thrush *Turdus philomelos* (Widespread breeding summer visitor and passage migrant; small numbers overwinter, mainly in coastal areas.)
Although numbers have declined in the second half of the twentieth century, the return of the breeding population from their wintering quarters in Ireland and south-west Europe is still one of the notable events of the early spring. Although some appear in February, the main arrival is usually

in early March. Territories are occupied immediately.

After the breeding season local birds remain to take advantage of the rowan crop. In September and October they are joined by migrants of the Continental race from Fenno-Scandinavia.

Wintering birds in eastern coastal villages appear, from the richness of their colouring, to be local residents rather than immigrants, which presumably move much further south. There were at least six in the Stoer area after hard frosts in late December 1996.

A leucistic male returned to Dornoch each summer from 1965-67.

Redwing *Turdus iliacus* (Scarce breeder in variable numbers; mainly passage migrant and winter visitor.)
Redwings were first proved to breed in Sutherland in 1925 and have probably done so more or less continuously ever since. As they occupy a wide variety of woodland habitats, from birch woods and alder carr to pine plantations, many pairs are probably overlooked and the population is probably considerably higher than the 30-50 pairs generally accepted. In good years it may be well into three figures. At least 17 pairs bred around Lairg alone in 1983. It is apparent that numbers fluctuate from year to year, probably in response to spring temperatures and the incidence of easterly winds over the North Sea during the northward migration.

Spring passage, which continues into early May, is relatively slight. In the west it certainly involves birds of the Icelandic race. In the autumn the vast majority of birds are of Scandinavian and Russian origin, although Icelandic birds also pass through. The first flocks can occur in late September but the main arrival is in October, when hundreds, sometimes thousands use the east coast fly-way. Some divert to take advantage of inland feeding opportunities. At least 5000 flew south-west on 15 October 1996, with a further 3000 grounded in the Brora area. Over the next few days an estimated 20-30,000 birds were present in south-east Sutherland with similar numbers in Strath Halladale (and presumably other parts of the north).

Even these numbers were eclipsed by an extraordinary passage on 30 October 1995. Flocks were first noticed flying south west through the Clynelish valley, Brora, at 11.00 GMT. These soon merged into a

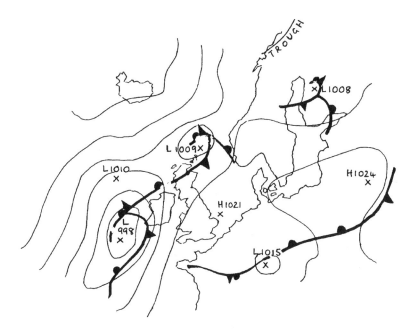

Simplified synoptic chart for 06.00 GMT on 30 October, 1995.
A ridge of high pressure over southern Scandinavia allowed Redwings
to depart to the south-west overnight. A depression and associated
weather front over the northern North Sea forced them down
and concentrated them along the east coast fly-way.

continuous stream which lasted, unbroken, for over an hour and at its
peak was three layers deep. Constant monitoring of the rate of flow past a
fixed point over four hours produced a very conservative estimate of
125,000 birds. This is the largest count ever made in Britain. Despite
heavy evening rain the passage continued (uncounted) until at least mid-
night. Another 10,000 followed early the next morning.

Numbers are normally small in mid winter, with parties of up to 50 or
so confined to coastal areas and the lower straths.

Mistle Thrush *Turdus viscivorus* (Mainly breeding summer visitor; a few
winter in lowland areas.)
This species underwent a dramatic range extension in Scotland in the
nineteenth century and, by the 1880s, was breeding right up to the north

coast. Further population increases in the twentieth century have been aided by afforestation in previously treeless tracts. Now, this is the commonest thrush of the hinterland in summer, although it is still relatively scarce in the west.

The species propensity for autumn flocking is well known. There were hundreds in the south east in early October 1991, with some south west movement apparent on the east coast fly-way on 5th. Winter numbers are small, with birds confined mainly to coastal areas and the lower straths.

Grasshopper Warbler *Locustella naevia* (Scarce and irregular summer visitor; has bred.)
Although this species readily colonises young plantations, too few reach Sutherland to take advantage of the abundance of suitable habitat. Numbers fluctuate, probably depending on spring weather conditions. Most birds are probably overshooting migrants which sing for a while but remain unpaired, although breeding has been proved in the west and two were seen near Melvich on 4 June 1988. Occurrence seemed to be more regular in the late 1960s and early 1970s. Now, it is at best uncommon and in several recent years none has been reported. The earliest date is 3 May. There are no records after the cessation of song, the latest being one singing at Dornoch on 1 August 1969.

Sedge Warbler *Acrocephalus schoenobaenus* (Breeding summer visitor, passage migrant.)
Sedge Warblers breed fairly widely in scrub and marshes but are commonest in the south-east. Although numbers fluctuate markedly from year to year, there are indications that the species may have now recovered from the losses sustained on its African wintering grounds during the Sahel drought in the late 1960s. The first breeding on Handa occurred in 1975. Exceptional numbers were reported from the Dornoch area in 1982.

The earliest record is from Clynelish Moss, Brora on 6 May 1995. Surprisingly, there are no recent records later than 31 August, although it occurs in Caithness and the Northern Isles well into September.

Icterine Warbler *Hippolais icterina* (Scarce passage migrant; potential breeder.)
A singing bird was reported from Loch Merkland in late May 1994 and another was tape recorded at Laxford Bridge on 25 June 1995. In the light of the recent successful nesting at Creag Meagaidh, the species may soon breed in Sutherland. The only other records are of single juveniles in autumn: at Melvich on 4 September 1992 and on 22 and 28 September 1980, and at Lothbeg Point on 27 September 1996.

Subalpine Warbler *Sylvia cantillans* (Vagrant from southern Europe.)
A male at Durness on 28 August 1989 is the only record.

Barred Warbler *Sylvia nisoria* (Scarce autumn passage migrant.)
An immature was trapped at Melvich as early as 14 August 1982. One there on 31 August 1985 stayed until 17 September. Four different immatures were seen at three other north coast sites from 4-6 September 1975 (one remaining until 10th). Single immatures also occurred at Melvich on 4 September 1983, 9 September 1995, 11 September 1992 and from 7-16 October 1983. The latest record (and the only one from the southeast) is from Clyne Milton, Brora on 20 October 1991.

Lesser Whitethroat *Sylvia curruca* (Scarce passage migrant, mainly, spring.)
The recent northward spread of breeding birds in Britain is reflected in an

increase in Sutherland records. Angus (1983) listed six records of single birds in the years 1969-77, all between 31 May and 28 June. Since 1985 there have been a further ten spring and early summer records from the north-west (six), north (two) and south-east (two) from 20 May to 21 June.

There have also been six autumn records, all from the north and north-west, between 13 September and 22 October.

Whitethroat *Sylvia communis* (Breeding summer visitor and passage migrant.)
It seems the Whitethroat was never common in Sutherland. Surprisingly, therefore, the effects of the Sahel drought in the late 1960s, whilst noticeable, were not as severe as in southern Britain (MacDonald 1979), suggesting that the northernmost breeders were not wintering in the worst affected areas. Most recent breeding records are from the south-east but it also occurs in the west and, sparingly, in the north. About a quarter of pairs may rear second broods in some years (MacDonald 1979).

The main arrival is in mid May, one at Brora on 24 April 1993 being unusually early. A large 'fall' of Scandinavia-bound migrants in late May 1996 included exceptional numbers, with over 20 between Helmsdale and Golspie from 20th. This arrival did not appear to result in a significant increase in the number of breeding pairs that summer. Autumn migrants, or late broods, remain into early September (latest 12th).

Garden Warbler *Sylvia borin* (Scarce breeding summer visitor in the south; passage migrant.)
This species extended its breeding range northwards beyond the Grampians in the second half of the twentieth century. It was not heard in Sutherland until 1951. Singing males have been more or less annual in the south of the county from the early 1980s, but breeding was not finally proven until 1992, when birds were seen carrying food to young at West Clyne, Brora in July. Singing birds are occasionally heard further north and west (e.g. Melvich from 25 May 1994, Achmelvich on 31 May 1988 and Loch Naver on 28 June 1984).

Most arrive in the second half of May (earliest 15th). A few were associated with a large 'fall' of migrants from 22-26 May 1996. One on

Handa on 11 June 1982 was presumably a late migrant.

Trapping at Melvich has shown the species to be a regular migrant on the north coast in autumn, from mid August through September. There are also odd records from the west and south-east during this period. One at Balnakeil on 1 October 1982 is the latest.

Blackcap *Sylvia atricapilla* (Scarce summer visitor, passage migrant and winter visitor.)
The incidence of singing males in the south of Sutherland has increased in recent years, although proof of breeding is still lacking. A juvenile trapped at Melvich on 26 July 1982 is unlikely to have been of local origin.

One was heard at West Clyne, Brora on 21 April 1995 but most do not arrive until May. Spring migrants occasionally reach the north coast, and Handa in the west.

Autumn passage is mainly in October. One ringed at Dungeness, Kent on 25 September 1977 was controlled at Melvich two weeks later. This gives credence to the theory that some Continental Blackcaps move north to winter and that these, rather than Scandinavian breeders, account for the small but significant wintering population in coastal villages. There are records from Lochinver, Durness and the north coast as well as the south-east.

Pallas's Warbler *Phylloscopus proregulus* (Vagrant from Siberia.)
The only record is of one at Keoldale, Kyle of Durness, on 15 October 1989.

Yellow-browed Warbler *Phylloscopus inornatus* (Rare autumn passage migrant.)
There are only five records, three of which were trapped at Melvich: on 6 October 1979, 11 October 1978 and 14 October 1986. There was one at the Kyle of Durness from 6-9 October 1988 and one at Scourie on 7 November 1980.

Dusky Warbler *Phylloscopus fuscatus* (Possible vagrant from Siberia.)
A brown phylloscopus with a prominent pale supercilium, seen by

First and last dates of the breeding warblers

	Earliest	Latest
Sedge Warbler	6 May	31 August
Whitethroat	24 April	12 September
Garden Warbler	15 May	1 October
Wood Warbler	2 May	8 October
Chiffchaff	21 March	13 November
Willow Warbler	8 April	21 September

Iain MacDonald in a mixed bird party at The Mound on 20 November 1994, was most probably of this species.

[Bonelli's Warbler] *Phylloscopus bonelli* (Possible vagrant from Europe.) After a 'fall' of migrants on 26 May 1996, near Helmsdale, the author had a close flight and a distant perched view, of a robust, pale headed *phylloscopus* which was strikingly yellow on the rump. This species has been extending its breeding range north into northern Europe and there has been a corresponding increase of records in southern Britain in recent years.

Wood Warbler *Phylloscopus sibilatrix* (Breeding summer visitor, usually in small numbers, and scarce passage migrant.)
Wood Warblers spread north into northern Sutherland during the first half of the twentieth century in parallel with the colonisation of southern Norway and they now reach the north coast in good years. The species prefers mature, deciduous woodland and, consequently, is localised in its distribution. Numbers fluctuate (1984 and 1994 were bumper years). Angus (1983) states erroneously that it arrives in mid April. The earliest date is 2 May and most birds arrive in mid May.

There are few records of migrants. One was trapped at Melvich on 27 May 1994. In autumn, there were singles at Melvich on 11 August 1992, Handa on 25 August 1985, Melvich on 26 August 1988 and an unusually late bird there on 8 October 1988.

Chiffchaff *Phylloscopus collybita* (Summer visitor, occasional breeder and passage migrant in small numbers.)
Sutherland lies at the northern fringe of the species' British breeding range. It was not heard in the county until 1952 but is now annual in small numbers, with birds reaching the north coast in good years. The first proven nesting was at Skibo in June 1968. The species probably now breeds regularly at one or two favoured sites in the south, although singing males are not necessarily paired. A pair probably nested at Melvich in 1986, when there were larger than usual numbers in the county.

The first birds normally arrive in the first half of April, occasionally late March (earliest 21st). Numbers of migrants in both spring and autumn are small, but the records are well scattered. There was one at Durness on 30 October 1982 and stragglers have been recorded into November, including one at Golspie on 13 November 1995.

Willow Warbler *Phylloscopus trochilus* (Abundant breeding summer visitor; passage migrant.)
After Meadow Pipit, the Willow Warbler appears to be the most numerous breeding passerine, partly because its distinctive descending song makes it so conspicuous. The first birds normally arrive in mid April (earliest on Handa 8 April 1989), although they can be later in cold springs. The main arrival takes place in late April or early May. Trapping at Melvich showed a marked decline in numbers in 1991 from which the species was slow to recover locally.

'Falls' of migrants in spring can include relatively large numbers of Willow Warblers, such as that from 20-22 May 1996, when there were dozens in coastal bushes between Brora and Navidale. A bird on Handa on 8 May 1985 showed the characteristics of the eastern race *acredula*. Post-breeding dispersal probably accounts for the appearance of most of the young birds on coasts and in gardens in late July and August. Genuine migrants are normally rather scarce in autumn although there was a large 'fall' during strong easterlies in mid September 1996. Few are seen after the third week of September.

Goldcrest *Regulus regulus* (Common breeding resident and passage migrant.)

Goldcrests have benefited from the spread of conifer plantations and are abundant in places. Over 100 pairs nest in Balblair and Ferry Woods, Loch Fleet (Vaughan 1991). Their numbers fluctuate, mainly in relation to the harshness of the winters and the size of autumn influxes from Scandinavia. The latter can be large – Harvie-Brown and Buckley (1887) refer to a huge arrival in the autumn of 1882. More recently there have been notable influxes in 1982, 1988 (when ringing totals at Melvich in September/October were more than twice the norm), 1992 and 1996. A bird ringed at Melvich on 4 September 1983 was controlled at Spurn Point, Humberside, on 6 October 1983.

Spring passage is less obvious but the odd birds reach Handa in April, where there were 4 on 5 April 1985.

Firecrest *Regulus ignicapillus* (Scarce passage migrant and winter visitor.)

Firecrests have been steadily extending their breeding range northwards (reaching southern Britain in the early 1960s). There was one at the Kyle of Durness between 25 October 1987 and 20 March 1988, up to five at Lothmore for over two months from 14 December 1972 and a male at Melvich for six weeks from 17 February 1990. These winter records, and that of an English-ringed bird recovered in Caithness, suggest that, like the Blackcap, part of the breeding population moves north to winter. Large stands of mature gorse (favoured by the Lothmore and Melvich birds) are available to them (but inaccessible to bird-watchers!) in many parts of Sutherland.

The only other records are of autumn migrants at West Clyne, Brora, on 28/29 September 1991 and Melvich on 18 October 1993 and 27 October 1980 (erroneously dated 11 September 1980 in *Sutherland Birds* (1983)).

Spotted Flycatcher *Muscicapa striata* (Common breeding summer visitor.)
One of the latest summer visitors to arrive, this species is widespread in a wide variety of open woodland habitats from late May. The first birds rarely appear before mid May (earliest 26 April 1983). Reports of local declines in the south-east and north may not represent more than annual fluctuations. A few migrants are associated with 'falls' in spring and autumn. Most of the breeders have left by early September (latest 19th).

Red-breasted Flycatcher *Ficedula parva* (Rare autumn passage migrant.)
This delightful species probably occurs on the north coast in autumn more frequently than the four records (of five birds) suggest. There was one at Melvich on 2 October 1976 (erroneously dated 25 October in *Sutherland Birds* (1983)), one at Laxford Bridge from 15-19 October 1995, one at the Kyle of Durness on 17 October 1988 and two at Durness on 30 October 1982.

Pied Flycatcher *Ficedula hypoleuca* (Scarce passage migrant; occasional breeder in the extreme south.)
Most breeding attempts are probably made following arrivals of displaced migrants during May easterlies, or by overshooters. In 1995, two females laid a total of 11 eggs in a nest box in Amat Wood but all were infertile. Unpaired males were seen near Rogart on 30 May 1994, by Loch Brora on 5 June 1995 and at Craggie Beg on 10 June 1982.

The occurrence of drift migrants in Sutherland is surprisingly infrequent. Two at a regular ringing site at Melvich in May 1985 were considered unusual. In persistent easterlies, there was a scattering of birds from 21-26 May 1996 from Forsinard to the extreme south-east – more than ten in total, including at least four in the Brora area. Autumn birds are equally scarce. A large 'fall' of migrants in September 1995 (when up to 25 were seen at Tarbatness, Easter Ross on 8/9 September) produced a few, including birds at Strathy Point and Laxford Bridge on 13 September 1995 (the latter staying until 29 September).

Long-tailed Tit *Aegithalos caudatus* (Fairly common breeding resident.)
Occurs throughout the county, wherever suitable woodland or scrub

exists. A brood was fed by three adults at Apigill in May 1984. Numbers fluctuate relative to the severity of the winters.

The species is most obvious in autumn when flocks roam noisily, sometimes independently and sometimes as part of mixed bird parties. Flock sizes are usually between 10 and 25 birds but there were estimated to be at least 50 in a mixed bird party at Loch Fleet on 28 August 1990.

In the past, birds of the white-headed nominate race have been seen in the west during the breeding season, but there are no recent records of this form.

Willow Tit *Parus montanus* (Rare visitor from southern Britain; has bred.) There have been no recent records of this fairly sedentary species, which has been declining in most of its Scottish range. There was one at Invercassley in April 1953, a pair near Bonar Bridge in late April 1973 and a pair bred near Golspie in the late 1960s (Angus 1983). The oft-quoted record from Cape Wrath (24 November 1949) clearly refers, from the description, to a male Blackcap.

Crested Tit *Parus cristatus* (Occasional breeder in the extreme south; rare straggler elsewhere.)
Sutherland lies on the northern fringe of the Crested Tit's range. The species' preference for open, mature woods of Scots Pine with a shrubby under-storey limits its breeding opportunities. Small numbers (perhaps about 20 pairs) breed in pine plantations in the extreme south and a few north to Shin Forest. Two at Loch Fleet on 26 August 1990 were thought to be juveniles and breeding was confirmed there in 1993. The native pinewood regeneration project centred on Amat Wood should be of longer term benefit.

Single birds have occurred in winter further north, such as Clynelish Moss (December 1978 and 1992) and Shinness (28 February 1995).

Coal Tit *Parus ater* (Common breeding resident.)
Like the Goldcrest, Coal Tits have greatly benefited from afforestation. They are abundant in the south-east, with up to 75 pairs nesting in Balblair and Ferry Woods, Loch Fleet (Vaughan 1991). The autumn of

1985 produced a bumper crop of 'resident' titmice – at Melvich Graham Crittenden trapped 32 compared with a nine year total of 11 from 1976-84. Tony Mainwood ringed almost 250 different individuals in three gardens in the Golspie area in winter 1994/95.

Blue Tit *Parus caeruleus* (Common breeding resident.)
Blue Tits are fairly widespread but scarce in the extreme north-west. The population fluctuates, major declines resulting from severe winters. Recent occurrences on Handa have been in August. As with other tit species, the autumn of 1985 saw unusual numbers in the north. These may have included some examples of the Continental/Scandinavian race, which occasionally reach the Northern Isles in small numbers.

Great Tit *Parus major* (Common breeding resident.)
This species was rare in the north of Scotland in the nineteenth century but extended its distribution northwards in the first half of the twentieth. It is now widespread in Sutherland but still outnumbered by its smaller congeners. Whilst the British race is sedentary, birds of the Continental race irrupt occasionally and may occur in the north and east. One on Strathy Point on 28 November 1985 is a likely candidate.

Treecreeper *Certhia familiaris* (Fairly common breeding resident.)
Treecreepers are widespread throughout a variety of woodland habitats. Although preferring native woodland, they have undoubtedly benefited from afforestation. Up to 14 pairs nest in Balblair and Ferry Woods, Loch Fleet (Vaughan 1991). In autumn and winter the species often joins mixed bird parties. It is unusual to see more than a family party in one place but Harvie-Brown and Buckley (1887) cite an occurrence of 'some dozens' together in the south-east in March 1882. The species first occurred on Handa in July 1975.

Golden Oriole *Oriolus oriolus* (Rare migrant.)
The dates of the four occurrences span only a week and are typical for a late spring overshooter from Europe: a female near Melvich, on 29 May 1990, a male in Strathnaver on 30 May 1972, a male at Tongue on 31

May 1978 and a male at Altnaharra on 5 June 1972 (possibly the Strathnaver bird).

Red-backed Shrike *Lanius collurio* (Scarce migrant and summer visitor; has bred.)
Like the Wryneck, which colonised Scotland as the southern British population declined to extinction, Red-backed Shrikes from the Scandinavian population began breeding in small numbers in the Highlands in the 1970s. In Sutherland, breeding probably occurred near Dornoch in 1985 (pair present in June/July and seen collecting food) and was proved in 1988 (male feeding a juvenile near Bonar Bridge on 8/9 August). There was another report of a breeding pair about this time near Knockarthur.
    Between 1969 and 1981 there were five records of single birds between 23 April (an exceptionally early bird near Lairg in 1969) and 13 June (Angus 1983). Since then a male was seen west of Lairg on 24 May 1995 and there are six sightings of unpaired birds in five other years, five of which were between 4-7 June.

Lesser Grey Shrike *Lanius minor* (Vagrant from southern Europe.)
The only record is of a bird at Kinbrace on 21 June 1976.

Great Grey Shrike *Lanius excubitor* (Scarce winter visitor, passage migrant.)
This striking immigrant from Scandinavia is unpredictable in its appearances and, unfortunately, seems to have 'gone out of fashion' in the last ten years. There was a good run of records in the early 1980s including individuals at four localities in 1982 between 30 October and 9 December, a spring migrant at Strathy on 24 April 1983 and singles in November 1984 and 1985. Since then the only records are of one near Carbreck, Strath Dionard, on 17 October 1988 and one at Migdale on 7 November 1990.

Woodchat Shrike *Lanius senator* (Vagrant from southern Europe.)
The first record was of an adult at Craggy, near Forsinard, on 25 June 1996. This was quickly followed by a second: a juvenile at Balnakeil on 13/14 September 1996.

Jay *Garrulus glandarius* (Vagrant.)
Although the Jay is common in south-west Scotland and breeds as far north as Aberdeenshire in the east, the British populations of this species are sedentary. There are only two reports from Sutherland: one at Dornoch on 23 September 1944 and one in the Borgie Forest on 3 July 1975. Continental populations are occasionally irruptive and both of the above birds may well have been of Continental origin. (1975 was an irruption year.)

Magpie *Pica pica* (Former breeder; now very scarce.)
Magpies were common in the south-east of the county in the mid nineteenth century, but ruthless extermination by game interests had rendered it scarce before the start of the twentieth century. It ceased to breed in the south-east around 1920. Today, odd birds occur from the south-east to the north coast, mainly in spring. In the west, there was one on Handa on 12 April 1987 and one at Lochinver on 15 April 1986 and one at Achfary on 24 April 1984. One or two have been resident in the Melvich area since 1990 and three individuals were seen there in 1993. A pair near Brora in spring 1994 failed to breed.

Chough *Pyrrhocorax pyrrhocorax* (Former breeder.)
The Scottish range of this species contracted markedly in the early nineteenth century. There have been no records of the Chough in Sutherland since St. John saw some on the north coast in 1848.

Jackdaw *Corvus monedula* (Common breeding resident, but more local in the hinterland and the west.)
The species is abundant in the south-east. Large winter flocks of up to 3000 birds (usually associated with Rooks) may include some immigrants from the Continent. Local movements of tight flocks to and from the hinterland through, for example, Strath Brora have been noted, most often in late winter. These are probably related to feeding and roosting but suggest a different feeding strategy, perhaps linked to livestock distribution, by a part of the Jackdaw population not associating with Rooks.

Some south-westerly movement over the sea occurs, with Rooks, off the south-east coast from late September to November.

Rook *Corvus frugilegus* (Local breeding resident, mainly in the south-east, and winter immigrant.)
National surveys of rookeries were carried out in the mid 1940s and 1975. Despite a decline in the overall Scottish population between 1946 and 1975, the number of nests in Sutherland (2110) had increased by over 40% during this time. Of the 31 rookeries, all but three were east of Lairg. A census in 1995 indicates some decline from the 1975 position: an overall loss of four rookeries and a 27% reduction in the number of nests (Bremner and MacDonald 1996). Four on Handa in June/July 1991 were unusual.

Late autumn/winter flocks of over 1000 birds are not unusual and roosts of several thousand birds are found at Golspie and Invershin. In the north, there is a smaller roost at Tongue.

Large coastal movements in the south-east are mainly related to feeding and roosting but south-west movement over the sea in October/November undoubtedly involves immigrants, possibly from as far as western Russia. These may also account for most of the autumn and winter records away from rookeries in the north and west.

Hooded/Carrion Crow *Corvus corone* (Common breeding resident and passage migrant.)
The relentless march of the Carrion Crow northwards is restricting the 'pure' Hoodie population to the harshest parts of the hinterland and the north-western extremities of Sutherland. Winter flocks of Hoodies have exceeded 100 birds in the north and 50 in the west in the recent past. In the south-east, Carrion Crows and hybrids now comfortably outnumber Hoodies. There was, for example, a flock of 23 Carrions near Sciberscross, Strath Brora, on 13 January 1994. In 1983 a Carrion at Altnaharra was worthy of note. Now the black invader has reached the north coast, with birds at Strathy and up to seven south of Melvich in autumn 1996.

Movements of both forms, possibly only local, occur in winter and spring. Nineteen Carrion (plus two hybrids) flew south-west through the

Clynelish valley, Brora, on 6 January 1992 and six Hoodies followed the same route on 6 February 1995. Migrant Carrion Crows occur almost annually on Handa, mainly in spring. In autumn, a small south-westerly movement of Carrions was noted at Brora between 2 and 16 October 1991, with four Hoodies on 3 October.

Raven *Corvus corax* (Breeding resident.)
Despite heavy persecution in the nineteenth century and, more recently, the spread of afforestation in central Sutherland, Ravens are still thinly distributed over most of the county. Although some traditional sites have been abandoned in the south-east, there is no positive evidence of a serious recent decline in the overall population, which probably totals about 70 pairs, 30 of which are coastal (D A Ratcliffe).

Concentrations occur outside the breeding season, maxima 100 at Dalchork on 20 August 1985, 25 in Strath Brora on 4 January 1992 (compared with a roost of over 100 birds there in the 1870s) and 56 south-east of Kinbrace on 10 September 1996.

Starling *Sturnus vulgaris* (Common breeding resident, passage migrant and winter immigrant.)
This is another species with a surprisingly recent history in Sutherland, most of which was not colonised until the early part of the twentieth century. Harvie-Brown and Buckley (1887) described the Starling as rare prior to 1870 but 'abundant' at Scourie, Handa, the Badcall Islands, Durness and Tongue in the 1870s and 1980s. Curious, then, that the 'first' recent breeding on Handa occurred in 1973. Starlings are now widespread, with the exception of the treeless tracts of the hinterland, but the total population is not large compared to further south and is subject to fluctuation.

Scottish breeding birds are fairly sedentary. In spring, birds have been noted moving north-east through the Clynelish valley, Brora, in March and April. Post-breeding dispersal of south-eastern birds also seems to be mainly to the north-east, into Caithness. Migrants from Scandinavia pass through in late autumn. Numbers are modest in mid-winter, when flocks are mainly confined to coastal areas.

Rose-coloured Starling *Sturnus roseus* (Rare migrant from western Asia.)
This exotic species reaches western Asia and south-eastern Europe in variable numbers in late spring. A few 'overshooters' regularly reach Britain and, although the situation is complicated by escapes from captivity, the dates of the Sutherland records are all consistent with natural vagrancy. Angus (1983) lists records from June 1971, July, August and September 1972 and July 1976. Since then there have been a further seven reports of at least five adults: one at Stoer from 18-23 July 1995, possibly the same bird at Balnakeil on 3 August 1995 and Clashmore (Stoer) from 29 August, one at Dornoch for over a fortnight in August 1996, one in the north-west from 24 August-15 October 1989, one at Duart Mor (south of Scourie) on 6 September 1996 and one at Portskerra on 27 October 1988, which stayed for two weeks.

House Sparrow *Passer domesticus* (Local breeding resident.)
House Sparrows expanded their range in the twentieth century, even reaching Cape Wrath. They are now found in all the major towns and villages on coasts and in the larger straths, but they are still absent from much of the hinterland. The species is rarely seen away from its breeding areas but occasionally reaches Handa.

Tree Sparrow *Passer montanus* (Former breeder; now scarce.)
Sutherland lies on the northern fringe of the Tree Sparrow's range and the effects of its periodic fluctuations are therefore dramatic. The species bred widely but locally in the county in the late nineteenth century but had virtually disappeared by the 1930s. Following a range expansion in the 1960s, it bred sparingly in the south-east and occurred elsewhere but sightings again became increasingly irregular in the 1980s. One was seen by Balblair Wood, Loch Fleet on 14 May and 24 June 1988 and there were 4 there on 30 May 1989. Since then the only records are from the Dornoch area, most recently one from 28 April-13 May 1995.

Chaffinch *Fringilla coelebs* (Common breeding resident, passage migrant and abundant winter visitor.)
The Chaffinch vies with Meadow Pipit for the honour of being the

commonest passerine. The summer population is certainly less numerous, but it is much more abundant in winter when local birds are augmented by immigrants from Scandinavia and the Continent.

The resident population is widespread in all types of woodland, including urban and rural gardens. In the latter it, together with the Greenfinch, occupies the House Sparrow's niche. In winter the local breeders do not move far and, except in severe weather, do not seem to join the large flocks of immigrants, often several hundred strong, which are male dominated.

Passage birds are most obvious in autumn, when moderate to large numbers pass south-west along the east coast fly-way in late September and October. Southerly movement across the Moray Firth is also sometimes evident in hard weather in mid winter.

Brambling *Fringilla montifringilla* (Passage migrant and winter visitor in variable numbers; has bred.)
The first proven nesting of this species was in 1920 when a pair laid seven eggs. The nest was robbed. Since then, adults on territory have been noted in several years, most recently in 1993 (in the north). In 1996 a female came to a bird table in the south-east several times in June.

The number of Bramblings wintering in Sutherland is usually fairly small. In the past flocks of over 100 have occurred in the south east (maximum 200 at Embo on 23 February 1986). In recent years, parties have been typically of less than ten, but there were 50 at Dornoch on 5 February 1993.

Spring migrants start to move through in March and small numbers are recorded until early May. The numbers of autumn migrants were also thought to be small until regular watching on the east coast fly-way showed that a considerable through passage exists in October, at least in years when large numbers reach the Northern Isles. The largest count is of 260 flying south-west through the Clynelish valley on 20 October 1996. Another 63 followed a week later. There were unusually large numbers in the Melvich area in November 1994, where 22 were trapped.

Greenfinch *Carduelis chloris* (Common breeding resident, mainly in the south-east and north.)

The British populations of this species are fairly sedentary. Flocking occurs after the breeding season, when up to 150 have been seen in the Brora area. Smaller flocks feed behind beaches and in dunes in winter. In most rural gardens Greenfinches replace House Sparrows as the most aggressive feeders. It remains scarce away from the main settlements in the west and did not occur on Handa until 1975.

Some immigration is indicated by the control of a Norwegian-ringed bird at Golspie in November 1994.

Goldfinch *Carduelis carduelis* (Breeding resident and passage migrant; small numbers overwinter.)
Numbers of Goldfinches fluctuate in relation to the severity of the winters and the dryness of the summers (wet summers producing a poor seed crop). Formerly scarce, the species is not uncommon in the south-east now, where it has bred regularly since 1979, or on the north coast. Elsewhere, most records are of wandering birds in winter or migrants. 30 at Loch Evelix on 26 March 1994 is the largest spring flock.

Autumn numbers peak in late September/early October, maxima 45 at Brora on 19 September 1996, 60 on 30 September 1992, 75 there on the same date in 1994 and 45 on 29 October 1993.

A small south-westerly movement has been noted through the Clynelish valley from September to early January, including eight on 8 December 1993, ten on 31 December 1991 and 16 on 5 January 1993. The largest winter flocks are of 18 at Brora on 24 December 1993 and 20 near Melvich on 27 December 1994.

Siskin *Carduelis spinus* (Breeding resident and passage migrant.)
Although a major beneficiary of afforestation, numbers of Siskins fluctuate markedly from year to year in relation to seed abundance. The species is common in the south and in forested central and northern areas, but is still relatively scarce in the west. Juveniles were on the wing as early as 26 April at Bonar Bridge in 1985. Second broods fledge as late as the end of August.

Wintering birds are joined by arrivals from the south in April, as demonstrated by numerous ringing controls at Golspie (where a record

Goldfinches in south-east Sutherland

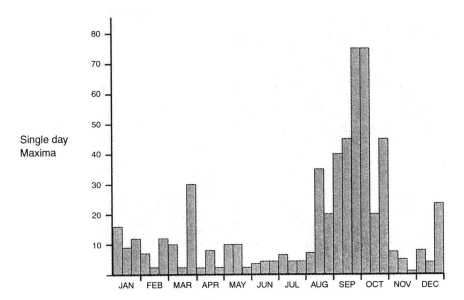

940 were trapped in April/May 1993) and influxes at Scourie in 1986 and
Melvich in 1993.

Post-breeding dispersal begins in July. Flocks of up to 250 birds assemble in autumn and winter. These may include a large proportion of immigrants since ringing has shown that many local birds winter in southern Britain. Two Golspie-ringed birds have been recaptured in the Netherlands and another in Belgium. Passage along the east coast fly-way is normally slight but there was an exceptional movement in 1993 when birds were moving south-west through the Clynelish valley at the rate of 300 per hour on 17 October, passage continuing at a reduced level until 24 October.

Linnet *Carduelis cannabina* (Breeding resident.)
Linnets are widely distributed in the south and north, wherever they have access to lowland cultivation, but are more local in the hinterland and in the west, where they are mainly summer visitors. Post-breeding flocks assemble from July, maxima 200 at Clynelish, Brora on 16 January 1995 and 300 at Skelbo Street on 7 March 1993.

Some local birds probably move south in the winter.

The number of immigrants is thought to be small and, although a small south-westerly movement was noted at Brora on 7 October 1995, there is no evidence for large scale passage through the county.

Twite *Carduelis flavirostris* (Breeding resident.)
Twites are widely, but thinly, spread throughout the county. In the absence of any baseline data, it is impossible to say whether the Sutherland population is in decline, as in other parts of Scotland, but a reduction in traditional crofting cannot have helped.

Movements to the hinterland from the coast begin in March. Breeding densities are low in moorland but up to 47 were counted on Eilean nan Ron in late July 1992. The species is scarcest in the south-east although a few pairs breed on the East Sutherland Hills and on the coast between Dunrobin and the Ord of Caithness.

Winter flocks of up to 400 birds occur in both coastal and inland areas. These may include some immigrants from Scandinavia.

Redpoll *Carduelis flammea* (Breeding summer visitor (cabaret), passage migrant and winter visitor.)
Several races of the Redpoll occur in Sutherland, among which I include Arctic Redpoll (see page 27).

Lesser Redpoll *C. f. cabaret*
This small, dark race of the Redpoll extended its British range northwards in the first half of the twentieth century, reaching Sutherland in 1928. It has greatly benefited from afforestation. Breeding birds return from late March/early April. Post-breeding flocks normally peak in autumn, but there were 200 at Achnabourin as early as 20 June 1985. A newly-fledged juvenile was seen at West Clyne on 6 September 1994.

Most of 'our' breeding birds move south in late autumn, but flocks of Redpolls in the south-east in mild winters often contain some Lessers and most of the 250 in Strath Brora on 19 January 1993 were of this race, as were 130 (in much colder conditions) in December 1996.

Mealy Redpoll *C. f. flammea* (Winter visitor and passage migrant in variable numbers.)
Mealy Redpolls originate mainly in Fenno-Scandinavia, although birds of the Greenland race (*rostrata*) may also occur. In autumn, the first migrants pass through in October (earliest 7 October). Passage continues into November and further arrivals can take place during hard weather movements in winter, when Redpoll flocks are most likely, but not necessarily, to be of this race. Autumn numbers are usually fairly small. Counts of 80 in Strath Brora on 21 October 1992 and 90 there on 17 November 1993 were eclipsed by a spectacular influx in 1995. Numbers quickly built up to 250 by 15 November and 400 by early December with other flocks elsewhere in the county. Very hard weather in late December then drove them south.

The return passage in spring is small, and peaks in mid April, maxima ten at West Clyne, Brora on 17 April 1996 and 20 in Strath Brora on 24 April 1995. Intriguingly, there was a pair at a plantation near Durness (male song flighting) on 27 May 1996.

Arctic Redpoll *C. (f.) hornemanni* and *C. (f.) exilipes* (Rare winter visitor, passage migrant.)
Improved field techniques in separating Arctic from pale Mealy Redpolls have resulted in an increase in records in Britain in recent years. There was one at West Clyne, Brora on 26 January 1993, one at Loch Hope from 10-20 April 1986, one *exilipes* at Melvich on 29 September 1984 (trapped) and two at Strathy on 6 October 1995* (an autumn in which unprecedented numbers reached Britain). *Exilipes*, which breeds in Arctic Eurasia, is the most likely race to occur. The very 'frosty' Brora bird may have been of the race *hornemanni* from northern Greenland and Canada.

[Two-barred Crossbill] *Loxia leucoptera* (Possible vagrant from northern Eurasia.)
There have been no positive records of this irruptive species, but Harvie-Brown and Buckley (1887) refer to the sale of 'a pair' from the collection of Dr Seeley from Sutherland in 1874.

Crossbill *Loxia curvirostra* (Breeding resident and passage migrant.)
The difficulty in separating this species from the Scottish Crossbill (with which it can occur) makes assessment of the records problematical, but its preference for spruce gives it a larger potential range in Sutherland, particularly as the new forests mature. There are breeding records from southern, central and northern areas but little suitable habitat in the west. Numbers fluctuate in relation both to food crops and the scale of immigration. 72 in Borgie Forest on 21 February 1988 is the largest recent flock.

A few migrants are seen in most years from late June to October, mainly on the east coast fly-way. Larger movements take place in some years, such as 1990, when at least 300 passed through the Loch Fleet area in June/early July, and in 1993 when south-westerly movement was noted in early July (maximum 35 at West Clyne on 2 July) and mid October (maxima 50 at Golspie on 14t October and 24 at West Clyne on 19 October). There were four on Handa on 15 June 1990, up to 19 there in August 1990/91.

Scottish Crossbill *Loxia scotica* (Breeding (nomadic) resident in the south.)

This Scottish endemic is dependent on Scots Pine but utilises plantations of this species as well as remnants of the old Caledonian Forest. It occurs in smaller parties than *curvirostra*, typically of less than 15. Its appearances in any given area are unpredictable, depending on the seed crop.

The largest number recorded in recent years is up to 40 in Balblair Wood, Loch Fleet in spring/summer 1989. Parties wander quite widely in early spring. Two groups totalling 19 birds in a plantation above Kildonan, Strath Ullie, on 12 March 1995 left to the south-west over open moor.

Trumpeter Finch *Bucanetes githagineus* (Vagrant from the Mediterranean basin.)
This North African desert species began to spread north into southern Europe in the 1960s. Two 'overshooters' reached Britain in 1971, one of which was on Handa on 8/9 June. Since then there has been one further Sutherland record – a male at Balnakeil on 4 June 1992.

Common (Scarlet) Rosefinch *Carpodacus erythrinus* (Rare summer visitor and passage migrant; colonising from the east, and has bred.)
Four young were fledged from a nest in a raspberry patch near the north-west coast in 1990 – the first proof of breeding in the county and the first proven successful breeding in Scotland. The distinctive song of the male is becoming a more regular phenomenon and, given the rate of the species' recent range expansion on the Continent, it is likely to be a regular breeder before the new millennium is very old. Males were present at Lairg in June/July 77 and June 1978. There were then no reports until 1987 when a male sang in Golspie on 4 June. One was heard at the Doll, Brora on 31 May 1992 and a first summer male sang at Scourie on 24/25 June 1995. There were at least two males in the north-west in 1996.

Juveniles were seen in the Clynelish valley, Brora, on 15 September 1996 (with Greenfinches) and on the unusually late date of 11 December 1991 (flying south-west, calling).

Bullfinch *Pyrrhula pyrrhula* (Breeding resident and winter immigrant.)
Bullfinches are quite widely distributed although commonest in the south-east. They are most obvious in autumn and winter when feeding

flocks roam scrub, woods and gardens. Most flocks are of less than 20 but larger concentrations of up to 100 birds have been noted in the past.

Birds of the brighter northern race reach Scotland in autumn, sometimes in quite large numbers (as in 1994).

Hawfinch *Coccothraustes coccothraustes* (Scarce and unpredictable visitor, mainly in autumn.)

The erratic movements of this secretive finch defy analysis, but most of the Sutherland records are in October. Birds reaching Sutherland are as likely to be from the Continent as from the British breeding population. A recent increase in sightings, with multiples in 1996, suggest it is getting commoner, but this may be a temporary phenomenon.

Two at Cape Wrath on 15 October 1911 were the first for the county. It was next seen in 1977 – one near Achfary on 6 July. Since then there have been the following reports: 6 at Lothmore on 2 January 1996, three at Oldshoremore on 8 April 1983, four over the Harriet Plantation (south of Loch Fleet) on 13 October 1996, one at Melvich on 15 October 1995 and one near Brora on 22 October 1993.

Lapland Bunting *Calcarius lapponicus* (Scarce passage migrant and winter visitor.)

There are surprisingly few records of this sub-Arctic breeder, which bred in the Highlands in the 1970s. There are only four records from 4-10 September, maximum seven on Eilean nan Ron on 9 September 1962, plus one west of Lairg on 16 November 1983.

In mid winter, one flying south-west at Clynelish, Brora on 24 January 1994 and one at Littleferry on 22 February 1993 are the only sightings.

In spring, singles have been seen at Whiten Head on 21 March 1970, Dornoch on 3 April 1988, Handa on 27 May 1958 and Sheigra on 2 June 1972.

Snow Bunting *Plectrophenax nivalis* (Winter visitor and passage migrant in variable numbers; occasional breeder.)

The first proven breeding of this species in Scotland was on Ben More Assynt in 1886; it has been seen on various mountains in a number of years since, but 1974 is the last year in which breeding was confirmed.

In autumn, birds begin arriving from their Arctic breeding grounds in September (earliest 14 September). Numbers are normally modest but 'many thousands' were reported from Strathy Point on 30 November 1931. This must have been quite a spectacle! Some south-westerly movement occurs on the east coast from September to November and further movements are associated with severe weather in winter, e.g. 33 at Brora on 21 December 1991 and 18 on 27 February 1993.

Birds are widely distributed in winter, both on the coast and inland, but in several recent years there have been very few. The largest numbers recorded in recent times are, on the coast, 400 at Loch Fleet on 16 November 1973 and 300 at Dornoch on 15 February 1987 and, inland, 50 at Knockarthur on 30 December 1993 and in the Ben Armine area in late February/early March 1992.

Spring passage is less obvious and mainly effects the west and north. Small numbers have occurred on the north coast in March/April and on Handa from early April to early June. There were four on Foinaven on 9 May 1982.

Pine Bunting *Emberiza leucocephalos* (Rare winter visitor.)
This Asiatic counterpart of the Yellowhammer is spreading westwards and occurring with increasing frequency in Britain. There was a male in Golspie from 6-8 January 1976.

On 4 January 1995, a newly arrived flock of Yellowhammers on Clynelish Moss contained a bird lacking any yellow in the plumage which had a paler, brighter rump than its companions. It was almost certainly a female Pine Bunting.

Yellowhammer *Emberiza citrinella* (Breeding resident.)
Yellowhammers are still fairly common in parts of the south-east but it has declined locally, most notably in the Dornoch area. It is more patchily distributed in the west and is scarce in the north. Winter flocks of up to 20 (maximum 40 at Dornoch on 10 November 1995) are of unpredictable appearance and may include birds from outside the county.

Ortolan Bunting *Emberiza hortulana* (Rare passage migrant from Europe.)

Harvie-Brown and Buckley (1887) refer to a specimen obtained in Sutherland prior to 1842. In modern times there are three records, all in late spring: a female on Handa on 28 May 1996, a female there on 29 May 1985 and a male at Clo Mor on 9 June 1976.

Rustic Bunting *Emberiza rustica* (Rare passage migrant.)

There are two spring records of this north Eurasian breeder: a male at Cape Wrath on 11 May 1906 and a singing male at Baligill on 16/17 May 1991.

Little Bunting *Emberiza pusilla* (Vagrant from northern Eurasia, probably overlooked.)

One at Rosehall on 29 December 1979 is the only record. Its occurrence elsewhere in the Highlands suggests it should be looked for amongst winter finch flocks. The species should also occur as an autumn passage migrant, as it does regularly in the Northern Isles.

Reed Bunting *Emberiza schoeniclus* (Breeding resident and passage migrant.)

Widely but thinly distributed in marshy habitats. Most territories are occupied only from March/April, birds retiring to coasts or moving south for the winter.

Birds in the north and north-west in spring and autumn may include some migrants. One flying south-west through the Clynelish valley on 20 October 1996 (a day of large scale arrivals from Scandinavia) is the only evidence of diurnal passage. Winter parties may include immigrants from further north and east.

Red-headed Bunting *Emberiza bruniceps* (Probable escape.)

There was a male at Scourie on 13 May 1972, one at Crask from May 1989 into June and another on Handa on 1 June 1975.

Black-headed Bunting *Emberiza melanocephala* (Rare passage migrant/escape.)
Occurrences of this southern Eurasian breeder, which is expanding its range to the north-west, are becoming more frequent in Britain. There have been five records in Sutherland (all of males) since 1990: at Kinlochbervie on 28 May 1995, Handa on 29/30 May 1991, Scourie from 23-28 June 1990, Balnakeil on 30 July 1994 and Achrimsdale, Brora from 1-4 October 1994.

Corn Bunting *Miliaria calandra* (Former breeder; now rare.)
This species of agricultural land declined dramatically from the mid twentieth century. About 20 pairs still bred in the Dornoch area in the 1960s (MacDonald 1965), by which time it had disappeared from the north and west of the county. It ceased breeding at Dornoch in the early 1970s and was last recorded there in 1976. In recent years, one flew south-west at Brora on 17 February 1992, one was reported from Cape Wrath on 7 June 1994 and two were seen at Proncy (north of Evelix) on 19 July 1992.

[Lazuli Bunting] *Passerina amoena* (Probable escape.)
A male of this North American bunting was seen at Achfary in late May 1974.

References and Bibliography

Angus, S (Ed.) *Sutherland Birds,* 1983

Baxter, EV and Rintoul, LJ *The Birds of Scotland,* 1953

Bremner, DM and MacDonald, D Decline of Sutherland Rookeries, *Scottish Birds* 18 (1996), 248

Brown, L *British Birds of Prey,* New Naturalist Series, Collins, 1976

Burton, JF *Birds and Climate Change,* Helm, 1995

Green, RE The status of the Golden Eagle in Britain in 1992, *Bird Study* 43 Part 1 (1996), 20-27

Everett, MJ Breeding status of Red-necked Phalarope in Britain and Ireland *British Birds* 64 (1971), 293-302

Harvie-Brown, JA Extracts from the journal of a nesting tour in Sutherland, *Zoologist* (1868), 1305-1311

Harvie-Brown, JA and Buckley, TE *A Vertebrate Fauna of Sutherland, Caithness and West Cromarty,* 1887

Lack, P *The Atlas of Wintering Birds in Britain and Ireland,* 1986

Lloyd, C, Tasker, ML and Partridge, K *The Status of Seabirds in Britain and Ireland,* 1991

MacDonald, D Notes on the Corn Bunting in Sutherland, *Scottish Birds* 3 (1965), 235-246

MacDonald, D Further early fledging of Hen Harriers, *Scottish Birds* 7 (1972), 204

MacDonald, D Notes on the Whitethroat in Sutherland, *Scottish Birds* 10 (1979), 296-305

Nethersole-Thompson, D and Nethersole-Thompson, M *Greenshanks* 1979.

Pennie, ID A century of bird-watching in Sutherland, *Scottish Birds* 2 (1962), 167-192

Ratcliffe, DA *The Peregrine Falcon,* Poyser 1980

Ratcliffe, DA and Oswald PH (Eds) *The Flow Country: the peatlands of Caithness and Sutherland* NCC Publication, 1988

St. John, Charles *A Sportsman and Naturalist's Tour in Sutherlandshire,* 1849

Stoneman, J G and Willcox, NA Seabirds of Handa Island, *Scottish Birds* 18 (1995), 78-87.

Selby, PJ On the…birds inhabiting the county of Sutherland. *The Edinburgh New Phil. Journ.* 1836: 156-161, 286-295

Sharrock, JTR *The Atlas of Breeding Birds in Britain and Ireland*, T & AD Poyser, 1976

Stroud, DA , Reed, TM, Pienkowski, MW and Lindsay RA *Birds, bogs and forestry: the peatlands of Caithness and Sutherland*, NCC Publication, 1987

Swann, RL Highland Oystercatchers *Ringing and Migration* 6 (1985), 55-59

Thom, VM *Birds in Scotland,* Poyser, 1986

Thorpe, RI Spring passage of skuas at Handa, *Scottish Birds* 11 (1981), 224-226

Vittery, A Status of the two forms of Mediterranean Shearwater. *British Birds* 87 (1994), 189

Voous, KH (1977) List of Recent Holarctic Bird Species *Ibis* 119 (1977) 223-250; 376-406

Walker, AFG The moult migration of Yorkshire Canada Geese, *Wildfowl* 21 (1970), 99-104

Whitfield, DP Waders (Charadriidae) on Scottish Blanket Bogs: recent changes in numbers of breeding birds, in Parkyn *et al* (Eds) *Conserving Peatlands*, Centre for Agriculture and Biosciences, 1996

Yapp, WB Birds of the Northwest Highland Birchwoods, *Scottish Birds* 8 (1974), 16-31

Chronology of Events of Ornithological Significance

This resumé reminds us how quickly the status of birds can change. Species like Eider and Fulmar, which today are such common and integral components of the coastal scene, are in fact relatively recent colonists. A number of species, including the once locally common Corn Bunting, has ceased to breed, whilst the fortunes of others, particularly birds of prey, have fluctuated dramatically in response to changes in human attitudes.

1836 P. J. Selby's account of his tour of Sutherland (the first county bird list) published

1848 Eider proved to breed for the first time (at Tongue)

1849 Charles St. John published *A Sportsman and Naturalist's Tour in Sutherlandshire*

1855 Common Scoter proved to breed for the first time in Scotland

1868 A pair of Great Northern Divers almost certainly bred in Assynt
      Tree Pipit proved to breed for the first time

1875 Goosander proved to breed for the first time

c.1880 Osprey ceased to breed (last pair shot by Charles St. John)

1886 Snow Bunting proved to breed for the first time in Scotland

1887 Publication of Harvie-Brown and Buckley's *A Vertebrate Fauna of Sutherland, Caithness and West Cromarty* which included the first detailed review of the county's avifauna

1892 An irruption of Ruddy Shelducks into northern Europe included a party of five at Durness on 20 June (the first Scottish record) and up to 14 there during the next two weeks

1897 Fulmar proved to breed for the first time (at Clo Mor)

1901 White-tailed Eagle attempted to breed for the last time (the clutch was 'obtained')

1908 First recovery of a Sutherland-ringed bird (a Wigeon, ringed at Loch Brora in June and shot in the Netherlands that September)

1913 Gadwall proved to breed for the first time

1920 Brambling proved to breed for the first time

1925 Redwing proved to breed for the first time in Scotland

1929 Slavonian Grebe proved to breed for the first time

1931   'Tens of thousands' of Snow Buntings arrived at Strathy Point on
        30 November
1935   Tufted Duck proved to breed for the first time
1959   Wood Sandpiper proved to breed for the first time in Scotland
1961   Whimbrel proved to breed for the first time
1962   Dr Ian Pennie's review of 127 years of bird-watching in
        Sutherland published in *Scottish Birds*
        Handa Island nature reserve established
1964   Great Skua proved to breed for the first time (on Handa)
1966   Collared Dove proved to breed for the first time (at Dornoch)
1968   Arctic Skua proved to breed for the first time (on Handa)
        Chiffchaff proved to breed for first time
1970   Loch Fleet Nature Reserve established
        A Stilt Sandpiper at Dornoch on 18 April was the first Scottish
        record and the first spring record for Britain
1971   Scotland's first (and Britain's second) Trumpeter Finch was seen
        on Handa on 8/9 June
1973   A pair of Sanderlings was displaying on a northern mountain on
        15 June
1976   The rapid decline of the Corn Bunting (in progress since the
        nineteen sixties) was completed with the last report of a single
        bird near Dornoch
1980   Ruff proved to breed for the first (and so far the only) time
1983   'Sutherland Birds' published – a guide to the status and ecology of
        birds in the county
1987   'Birds, bogs and forestry: the peatlands of Caithness and
        Sutherland' published by the Nature Conservancy Council – a
        review of the importance of the 'Flow Country' for wildlife in the
        face of proposals for large-scale afforestation
1990   Scarlet (Common) Rosefinch proved to breed for the first time
1991   A White's Thrush at East Clyne, Brora on 27 September sparked
        the first mass 'twitch' to the county by birders from all over
        Britain.
1992   Garden Warbler proved to breed for the first time
        Ivory Gull (26 March) and Alpine Swift (21 July) recorded for the

first time.

1994   Goldeneye proved to breed for the first time
Kentish Plover recorded for the first time (27 May)
Unprecedented numbers of Long-tailed Skuas were seen off the east and north coasts from 9 August until 19 October (including at least 69 off Brora on 9 August)

1995   Forsinard Estate acquired by RSPB
Little Bittern recorded for the first time (8 May)
A south-westerly movement of Redwings along the east coast fly-way was conservatively estimated to involve at least 125,000 birds, with many more passing after dark – a British record

1996   Over 10,000 Little Auks flew north-east past Brora and Lothbeg Point on 6/7 January
Woodchat Shrikes (25 June and 13/14 September), Laughing Gull (13 August-mid October) and Water Pipit (23 October) were recorded for the first time

Donnie MacDonald – an appreciation

For over 60 years Donald ('Donnie') MacDonald has recorded the bird life of Sutherland, especially around his native Dornoch. Any student of birds in the county soon realises the wonderful contribution he has made. Bird behaviour, migrant dates, breeding biology and changes in the avifauna have all been faithfully noted. A genuine all-round naturalist, he enthuses as much about a previously unrecorded 'billing' display between male and female Blackbirds as he does about notable finds such as Buff-breasted and Stilt Sandpipers.

Donnie's diary starts on 1 January 1933. This was a time when bird-watching was far from the popular and 'acceptable' pastime it is now. Dr Ian Pennie, in his meticulously researched account of Sutherland birds over the last century, was able to list very few published records from the county between the end of the Harvie-Brown masterpieces and the late nineteen forties. Donnie's early contributions in the forties, published in *The Scotsman*, reflect an era when brevity was not paramount. One such note described the female Long-tailed Duck as 'a demurely clad bird lacking the artistic tail of her mate'.

Perhaps the most fascinating aspect of a lifelong study of the bird life of an area is the understanding it allows of even subtle changes. Donnie has recorded accurately the change in status of many species, amongst them Goldfinch, Whitethroat, Chiffchaff, Collared Dove, Grey Plover and, of course, Corn Bunting. In April 1946 he discovered a migration stop-over of Sandwich Terns on the Dornoch Firth. Half a century later these birds linger at exactly the same place.

His study of the Corn Bunting on farmland around Dornoch was an outstanding piece of research. Difficult nests to find in growing crops, this study is a superb example of what can be achieved by a dedicated amateur naturalist and stands easily alongside the work of Walpole Bond and Ryves from southern England. His work on Whitethroats assumed added significance after the crash of the species during the Sahel drought in the late nineteen sixties. Another oft-quoted note on the changing relative percentages of Carrion and Hooded Crows in the south-east of the county has had many imitators, but Donnie added scientific exactness to a familiar puzzle.

As a teenager I still recall one memorable June day when, searching with Donnie for a Linnet's nest, I was shown the nests of Whitethroat, Sedge Warbler, Wood Warbler and Corn Bunting. How easily he transmitted the challenge and excitement of bird-watching. Now, 64 years on from his first diary note, Donnie still retains his fascination for the natural history of his area. With infectious enthusiasm he recounts the difficulties a Whitethroat's nest posed him last year before he finally discovered it. At home that evening another BTO nest record card is started, maintaining his standing as the longest contributor to the BTO nest record scheme. A fitting achievement for a lifetime dedicated to ornithology.

Donald M. Bremner
Golspie, January, 1997

Useful Addresses

Colin Crooke (Recorder for Highland Region) c/o RSPB (see below).
Home address: 6 George Street, Avoch, Easter Ross, IV9 8PU

East Sutherland Bird Group
c/o Alan Vittery (see below). (Illustrated talks at the Community Centre,
Golspie High School, on the last Monday of every month from
September to March, except December – non-members welcome.)

Royal Society for the Protection of Birds (North Scotland Office)
Etive House, Beechwood Park, Inverness IV2 3BW. Tel: 01463 715000
(Fax: 01463 715315)

Scottish Natural Heritage (Local Area Office)
Main Street, Golspie, Sutherland KW10 6TG. Tel: 01408 633602
(Fax: 01408 633071)

Scottish Ornitholgists' Club
21 Regent Terrace, Edinburgh EH7 5BT. Tel: 0131 556 6042

Scottish Wildlife Trust
3 Carsegate Road North, Inverness. General enquiries to the Edinburgh
HQ – Tel: 0131 312 7765

Alan Vittery
164 West Clyne, Brora, Sutherland KW9 6NH. Tel: 01408 621827

Acknowledgements

Although Donnie MacDonald's special contribution to Sutherland ornithology is celebrated on page 157, another local 'grandee', Dr Ian Pennie, has also devoted a lifetime to Sutherland and Scottish ornithology, becoming a President of the Scottish Ornithologists' Club and contributing numerous papers to the literature.

On a more personal level, I am particularly indebted to Tony and Helen Mainwood, who provided unpublished data, reference material and much-needed computer assistance. The book would be much the poorer without Dave Pullan's excellent vignettes of typical Sutherland birds. Colin Crooke made numerous helpful comments on the draft text and provided a lot of new data. Graham Crittenden, Donnie MacDonald, Iain MacDonald, Derek Ratcliffe, Fraser Symonds and Tom Talbot also commented on the text and contributed unpublished data.

Will Beattie of the Forestry Authority supplied up-to-date statistics on planting. My wife, Bonnie, assisted with the drawing of maps and copying of weather charts.

Many others have contributed unpublished material or helped in other ways, including Geoff Bates, Roy Dennis, Brian Etheridge, Michael Fitch, Geoffrey Jordan, Janet Landles, Colin Leslie, Susan MacBeth, Mollie Mansfield, Peter Miller, Jim Oliver, Annette Parrott, Ken Purton, Susan Read, Roger Roseveare, Norrie Russell, Jeff Stenning, Julie Stoneman, Tim Stowe, Bob Swann, Fred Western, Philip Whitfield, Jim Williams and Valerie Wilson.

Finally, thanks (again) to Bonnie, who has borne the brunt of my extra hours in the field and at the PC with understanding (most of the time!).

Index of Species